THE SALTON COLLECTION

THE SALTON COLLECTION

RENAISSANCE & BAROQUE
MEDALS & PLAQUETTES

BOWDOIN COLLEGE-MUSEUM OF ART

BRUNSWICK, MAINE

MCMLXV

PREFACE

Few artifacts of any age have come down to us charged with the meaning of so many facets of their time as the Renaissance medal. Though relatively diminutive in size, they embody to an exceptional degree that fusion of art and thought which is one of the chief glories of the Renaissance. Indeed, in their beauty and their learning, these medals are a reflection in microcosm of the civilization which produced them. They represent a world which celebrated not only princes and prelates but poets and scholars as well, and they have been preserved down through the years by those who have cherished them as enduring expressions of the Humanistic tradition. ᵍ⁓ The present collection, one of the finest of its kind in private hands, belongs to Mr. and Mrs. Mark Salton of New York. The Salton Collection is particularly distinguished for the extremely high level of quality of the specimens in it; many of them, indeed, have come from the illustrious collections of the past. No fewer than seventeen examples are unique. While the origins of the Salton Collection date from before World War II, most of the pieces it now contains were collected since that time. Mrs. Salton has taken as great an interest as her husband in the formation of the collection, and her enthusiasm for, and knowledge of, medals is evident in her Introduction to the Catalogue. ᵍ⁓ The collection contains masterworks by the most important medallists of the Italian Renaissance, beginning in the Quattrocento with the founder and greatest exemplar of the art, Pisanello. He is represented by four medals, including his portrait of *Filippo Maria Visconti,* Duke of Milan (no. 1) and two of *Lionello d'Este,* Lord of Ferrara, one of which (no. 4) has as its reverse the celebrated study of Amor teaching a lion to sing. [A superb specimen of the portrait of *Pisanello* (no. 6) by Marescotti is also included.] Matteo de' Pasti has portrayed yet another Renaissance Prince, *Sigismondo Malatesta,* Lord of Rimini (nos. 10-13). These medals, because of their acutely perceptive characterization of personality and the ineluctable appropriateness of their design, convey a sense of the Renaissance Prince unsurpassed by any other record. ᵍ⁓ Also present is a piece by Goethe's favorite Italian medallist, Sperandio, of *Fra Cesario Contughi* (no. 17). A portrait of an ancient Roman, the *Emperor Caracalla,* may be seen on a work (no. 18) by the Venetian medallist, Boldù. Among the five medals in the collection ascribed to Spinelli are exceptional specimens of his portraits of *Vecchietti* and *Savonarola* (nos. 33 and 34). A most revealing portrait of *Mary of Burgundy* is on the reverse of a medal (no. 27) by Candida. Two medals, whose creators are unknown, are of extraordinary quality—a small rectangular bronze of an *Unknown Boy* (no. 8), possibly by a Ferrarese artist, and a very large one portraying the Florentine poet *Tito Vespasiano Strozzi* (no. 29), probably by a Florentine. Represented among the medallists of the Italian Cinquecento are Leoni, da Trezzo, Belli, and Cesati, the last of whom was greatly admired by Michelangelo. ᵍ⁓ The Salton Collection is particularly rich in the productions of the master craftsmen of the German Renaissance, including Christoph Weiditz, Friedrich Hagenauer, Joachim Deschler, and Valentin Maler, all of whom are famous for their intensely realistic portraits. Another member of this school was Hans Reinhart the Elder, who is best known for the strikingly three-dimensional effects of his silver medals. ᵍ⁓ Happily, in addition to medals of the Renaissance, this collection also contains a quantity of examples from the Baroque, a much less known period of medallic art. As a result, we are not deprived of the pleasure of such brilliantly executed portraits in gold as that of *Charles Emanuel I,*

Duke of Savoy (no. 43) by Gaspare Mola and *Pope Innocent XII* (no. 51) by Giovanni Hamerani. In addition, we can enjoy the French medals of Guillaume Dupré, including his remarkable work (no. 82), the obverse of which is a superb portrait of *Marcantonio Memmo,* Doge of Venice, and the reverse, an almost equally fine likeness of *Maffeo Cardinal Barberini,* later Pope Urban VIII. In Germany, among the great medallists of the period is Sebastian Dadler, First Goldsmith to the Imperial Court at Augsburg; in Holland, O. Wouter Muller, whose unforgettable portrait of *Admiral Tromp* is only half of a silver repoussé medal (no. 145), the other side of which is an elaborately pictorial naval engagement; and in England, Bernard Rantwic, whose likeness of *Sir Richard Shelley* (no. 151) holds an honored place among medallic portraits. ❧ Thirty-two plaquettes constitute a brilliant section of the Salton Collection. There is a *Pietà* (no. 156) by Agostino di Duccio, which is the only known specimen other than the one in the Louvre. L'Antico is represented by his portrait bust of the *Empress Faustina* (no. 157), and Riccio, by his *Judith with the Head of Holofernes* (no. 158) after Mantegna. Also particularly outstanding is Federigo Parmense's *Entombment* (no. 166), which is apparently unique and is here published for the first time. One of the most striking of the German plaquettes is another *Entombment* (no. 184), which is based on Dürer's composition of the same subject in his "Kleine Passion" series of engravings. The last of the plaquettes, a *St. Peter* (no. 187) by an unidentified Spanish artist probably working about the turn of the seventeenth century, is encased in wood and has a gilded scrollwork frame, illustrating the manner in which plaquettes frequently were adorned in earlier times. ❧ Finally, special mention must be made of four extraordinary pieces which do not, strictly speaking, fall into the category either of medals or of plaquettes. Two are portraits in stone—one of a nobleman, possibly *Cosimo de' Medici* (no. 36), mounted as a bijou, and attributed to Benvenuto Cellini or his school; and the other, of *Hieronymus Allgaeuer* (no. 109), by an unknown South German master, dated 1556. The third is a painted wax portrait of superb quality of an unidentified sixteenth-century *Nürnberg Patrician* (no. 100) mounted in an elaborately decorated fire-gilded bronze case of the same period. The last is a gold bolla (no. 169), probably unique (the British Museum's vast collection of seals contains only a sulphur cast), of *Andrea Gritti,* Doge of Venice, 1523-39. ❧ ❧ ❧ Several people have played an indispensable role in the production of this catalogue. My secretary, Mrs. Kathryn S. Rumsey, performed the extremely difficult task of typing the intricate catalogue entries with a vigilant eye for inconsistency and error. John McKee made the unusually sensitive photographs of the originals. For the superb design of the catalogue, we are profoundly indebted to Leonard Baskin. Our deepest thanks must, however, be reserved for the Saltons themselves for their vast knowledge of medallic art as manifested in the catalogue and for their great generosity in making their magnificent collection available to the public for the first time.

MARVIN S. SADIK
Director

INTRODUCTION

The aim of this introduction is to sketch in very broad outlines the development of the medal and the plaquette. The serious student who wishes to explore the field more profoundly will find that a very extensive body of specialized literature exists on the subject. ⁊ Antonio Pisano (c. 1397-1455, ac. as a medallist 1438-49) called Pisanello, a Veronese of Pisan origin and one of the most celebrated painters of his time, was to add further luster to his immortality when, in 1438, he produced the first Renaissance medal. The first person to be portrayed was the Byzantine Emperor John VIII Palaeologus (born 1390, Emperor 1425-48) who had come to Ferrara to attend the council for the reconciliation of the Eastern and Western Churches and to appeal for support against the Turks. ⁊ The medal was one of the arts which flourished during the Italian Renaissance because of the rebirth in Italy of interest in classical art—in this case, in ancient coins. The ancients, in addition to their coinage which served both as a medium of exchange and as a vehicle for propaganda, had, on occasions, struck very large but coin-like commemorative pieces, commonly called medallions. These, although official issues of the mints, were not primarily intended as money, but rather as rewards, gifts of grace or tribute, which were sometimes worn as decorations. Among the early Greek examples are the Athenian silver medallions (*dekadrachms*) struck in commemoration of the victory at Marathon (490 b.c.) and the Damareteion medallions coined 480/479 b.c. by the Syracusans out of the gold in a wreath presented by the defeated Carthaginians to Queen Damarete, wife of the Syracusan tyrant Gelon, when she obtained more favorable peace terms for them. ⁊ During the period of the Roman Empire the practice of issuing medallions was continued and developed extensively. The imperial portrait medallions, first coined during the reign of Octavius Augustus (63 b.c.-a.d. 14) and thereafter by many of his successors, portray exclusively the Emperor or members of his family. By the middle of the fifth century still another type of medallion made its appearance, the *contorniate*. Unlike the Greek and the Roman imperial medallions, the *contorniates* had no connection with the coinage. They were large copper pieces with raised borders, probably struck on the occasion of public games and exhibitions for presentation or sale to the spectators. On them we find represented victorious athletes and charioteers, mythological subjects, earlier emperors, and famous writers and poets such as Horace, Sallust, Apuleius, Terence, and others. The Roman portrait medallions and *contorniates,* glorifying some of the great men of antiquity, no doubt played a significant role in the development of the Renaissance medal, and it is probable that they were instrumental in inspiring Pisanello to depict in a similar fashion the men and women of his own time. Drawings by Pisanello after Roman pieces, made during his first stay in Rome while working in the Lateran (before he created his first medal), have been preserved (Louvre), attesting to his interest in those ancient works. ⁊ During the late Middle Ages there were a few isolated attempts at the revival of medallic portrayal. In Padua, a university city which throughout the Middle Ages had been dedicated to the tradition of classical learning, several medals were struck from engraved dies cut by an unidentified artist about 1390, commemorating the recovery of that city from Milanese hands. The portraits representing Francesco Carrara and his son, both Lords of Padua, are modelled after those on Roman imperial bronze coins, *sestertii.* From the same period, there exist other medal-like struck examples, products of a Venetian family of die-engravers, the Sesti.

ERRATA Owing to editorial, not author's, errors, the following corrections should be made in the INTRODUCTION.

Page [1], line 17: *For* out of the gold in a wreath *read* out of the proceeds from a gold wreath

Page [5], lines 31-34: *Read* A noteworthy example is a golden lion holding a cup containing a hundred gold medals presented to Anne of Brittany (born 1477, Queen 1491-1514) in March, 1494, upon her state entry into the city of Lyon accompanied by her husband, Charles VIII, who was on his way to the Italian campaign.

These pieces, perhaps to an even greater extent than the Carrara medals, imitate ancient coins. ⁊ Also of pre-Renaissance origin are a series of cast and chased medals (perhaps all or most of them made in two hollow shells subsequently joined together) depicting Roman and Byzantine emperors as well as other persons important in the early history of Christianity. These medals are believed to have been made in the late fourteenth century by Flemish-Burgundian goldsmiths and, together with a lead impression of the forementioned medal of the elder Carrara, were contained in the inventories of the collections of the great connoisseur, Jean, Duc de Berry (1340-1416). Old copies of only two medals from this series of mediaeval medallions have survived, portraying the Emperors Constantine the Great (c. 280-337) and Heraclius (c. 575-641). The style of both pieces reflects Flemish-Burgundian art at the end of the Middle Ages. ⁊ The medal proper, as conceived by Pisanello and as we know it now, was a creation of the Italian Renaissance. The general spirit of the age, with its humanistic aspirations and its stress on individualism, must have been very favorable to the development of the portrait medal, which was to reach an extremely high degree of popularity. ⁊ The early patrons of the Renaissance medal were chiefly the numerous art-loving princes of northern Italy, the various smaller and larger tyrants, and the ambitious condottieri, all of whom saw in it another means for their own glorification. Pisanello's example was followed almost immediately by other artists; the history of the medal in modern times had begun. ⁊ Soon persons from all classes of society—crowned heads, renowned statesmen, poets, artists, scholars, prosperous merchants, beautiful ladies, etc.—shared in the desire to see their features reproduced in "bronze eternal" and thus be immortalized. But it was not vanity alone which caused medals to be made; perhaps more important, medals were meant to be, and were treasured as, objects of art, offering enchantment to the eye and stimulus to the mind. As such they soon became objects of great interest to the collector. The Estes of Ferrara, besides having members of their own family portrayed on medals, arranged for the exchange of those bronze marvels with other reigning houses, and on occasions even ordered from their medallists portraits of some of their devoted servants. ⁊ Many other notables of that era: the Gonzagas of Mantua; the Sforzas of Milan; Alfonso, King of Naples; Pope Julius II; and the Medicis of Florence (who outshone them all) formed extensive cabinets of medals, some of which are preserved in museums today. But collecting was not confined to Italy: Jean, Duc de Berry in France; Konrad Peutinger (1465-1547) and his wife Margareta (Welser) in Germany; Erasmus in The Netherlands; to cite but a few illustrious examples, took pride and pleasure in assembling collections of medals and plaquettes. ⁊ As tokens of friendship and respect medals were presented to members of one's family or to friends; they were placed on tables, into vitrines, or pierced and suspended from a chain on the wall; medals were employed as ornaments on objects such as boxes and book covers and, notably in Germany, on tankards and other similar vessels. One of the best surviving examples is a splendid golden chalice Melchior Pfinzing had made in 1536; into its cover are set four medals representing Melchior himself as well as his three brothers, Sigmund, Seifridt, and Martin (Germanisches National-Museum, Nürnberg). As historic documents, medals were buried in the foundations of buildings, as is evidenced by examples found in the walls of the Rocca Malatestiana at Rimini, the Palazzo Strozzi, the Palazzo di Venezia, and others. ⁊ It also was fashionable on festive occasions to wear medals of suitable size as personal adornment; during the second part of the sixteenth century they sometimes had loops or chains attached, were hung with pearls or embellished with fine enamelled scrollwork. Three such "Bijoux" or "Gnadenpfennige" are in the present collection (nos. 36, 112, and 114). A number of paintings prominently record the luster medals lent to male and female attire. Lucas Cranach the Elder in 1533 executed the portrait of a Saxonian gentleman wearing a double necklace from which is suspended a medal of John Frederick the Magnanimous (1503-54, Elector of Saxony 1532-47) (formerly in the Wallraf-Richartz Museum, Cologne). In 1569, Ludger Tom Ring the Younger portrayed Gese Reiners of Brunswick, adorned by a necklace hung with a medal (Herzog-Anton-Ulrich Museum, Brunswick). ᛒ As a rule, the obverse of a medal shows the portrait, together with an inscription giving the name and title of the person represented, while the reverse usually bears an allegorical, historical, or (especially on German medals) heraldic design. A great many Italian artists were inspired by, and often freely borrowed their reverse motifs from, such classical works of art as the ancient group of the *Three Graces* now in the library of the Cathedral of Siena, or a group of horses from Athenion's (ac. c. 197-159 B.C.) gem of *Jupiter* thundering against the giants (Naples Museum). ᛒ A very popular reverse design on Italian Quattrocento medals was a personal device, the so-called *impresa,* an innovation of Pisanello. The *impresa,* usually with a legend, was chosen for its symbolic meaning, often obscure, alluding to the sitter's life, station, or accomplishments. It soon developed into a personal emblem of a sort, and numerous rules were formulated by learned men as to what constituted a suitable *impresa;* it had to be mysterious, while at the same time revealing to those who knew enough about the sitter. The humanist Angelo Poliziano (1454-94) reportedly complained that every bumpkin bothered him with requests for a secret device comprehensible only to his loved one, inscrutable to all others. The best known inventor of such riddles was Paolo Giovio (1493-1552) of Como, a historian of considerable erudition whose *Dialogue of Warlike and Amorous Devices,* first published in 1555, went into several editions within a few years. ᛒ The early Italian medals were invariably cast from wax models, a technique which, unlike the striking process employed for coins, did not impose limits on the size of the medal or the height of its relief. The kinds of waxes and other molding materials used differed according to artist and period. ᛒ The early method was as follows: a flat disk, usually of black slate, but sometimes of wood, bone, or glass, formed the base. On this the wax model was built up or carved out of a mass of wax. The latter method was probably employed by Pisanello. The two sides were modelled either on separate disks or on a single one. The finished model was then impressed into fine clay or into a paste made out of fine ashes, salt, and water. After the mold had been allowed to dry, the two halves were removed from the model, joined together, and the molten metal poured in. Additional specimens were made by forming a new mold over the first metal casting, as the wax model could seldom be used more than once; this was repeated as often as desired. The resulting second-generation casts in turn could serve for the preparation of new molds for still further specimens, and so on. However, due to the shrinkage of most metals in cooling, each successive cast became smaller. Sharpness of detail also would gradually deteriorate, and thus there is a marked difference in quality between an early and a late casting. The "lost wax" process also was used, though probably not by the early medallists. In this method the complete wax model was embedded in heat-resistant molding material; then, by heating the mold, the wax was melted out and the vacant space filled with molten metal. ᛒ When the mold was removed, it was usually necessary to chase the surface of the medal in order to remove casting imperfections such as air bubbles, edge ridges, and the like. If chasing was done to an excessive degree, or by less qualified hands than the artist's, or if "improvements" were attempted to the point of re-engraving, then the result was often such as to destroy the quality of the original design. ❧ A metal often used for the first casting, the "trial proof," was lead, owing to the ease with which it could be melted. The artist usually kept this first proof for future use and to demonstrate his skill to prospective clients. For subsequent casts, the medallists of the Quattrocento preferred bronze or related alloys. From the Cinquecento onward gold and silver were also used. ❧ The reddish color which bronze acquires when cast was considered too raw in appearance. The artist would, therefore, treat the finished cast with a lacquer or varnish to give it what is usually called "patina." The recipes for producing a patina were legion, producing tones ranging from light to deep brown, from brownish-yellow to green, and occasionally near-black. Sometimes medals were gilded or silvered; but unlike a patina to which age can only add beauty, such gold and silver coverings sometimes wore off. ❧ In Italy, medallic art reached its zenith during the Quattrocento, chiefly in Ferrara, Mantua, Venice, Florence, and Rome. To the medallists of that century we owe the finest portrait medals the Renaissance produced. ❧ Pisanello's influence was enormous. He was not only the founder of medallic art but also its greatest master. It is remarkable that even his first creation is a masterpiece. From 1438 to 1449 he produced a body of work which has never been surpassed in grandeur of conception and power of composition. There exists a portrait of Pisanello on a medal, formerly believed to be a self-portrait, but which now is ascribed to Antonio Marescotti (ac. 1444-62) of Ferrara (no. 6). ❧ Matteo de' Pasti (ac. 1441-68) was an immediate follower of Pisanello, perhaps even a pupil of the master. A native of Verona, he accompanied Pisanello to the court of Sigismondo Pandolfo Malatesta (died 1468) at Rimini. There De' Pasti made a number of medals of the tyrant of Rimini and of Isotta degli Atti, a woman of great intellect and personal charm who became Sigismondo's fourth wife. ❧ Sperandio (ac. 1466-c. 1504) of Mantua was among the most productive artists of the Quattrocento. For nearly forty years he enjoyed great popularity throughout northern Italy. His vigorous style must have pleased many patrons, judging by the number who sat for him. ❧ At Venice during the second half of the Quattrocento, one of the foremost medallists was Giovanni di Pasqualino Boldù (ac. 1454-c. 1477), whose works reveal a particularly strong affinity for antiquity. ❧ The name of Niccolo di Forzore Spinelli, called Niccolo Fiorentino (1430-1514), epitomizes Florentine medallic art at its height. No fewer than 130 medals have been attributed to him, of which five bear his signature. ❧ Toward the end of the Quattrocento there was a change in medallic style, as a result of the technical achievements of Gianfrancesco Enzola (ac. 1456-78) and Francesco Francia (c. 1450-c. 1517), who experimented with medals struck from engraved dies—a process similar to that of striking coins, though artistically more allied to engraving precious stones. Medallic art, formerly so intimately associated with sculpture and even painting, did not benefit from this more mechanical process. Fortunately, the best artists continued to favor casting, which continued into the Cinquecento, and indeed is still occasionally used. ❧ Foremost among the medallists of the Cinquecento was Benvenuto Cellini (1500-71). He is known to have engraved in hard materials, and the honestone portrait (no. 36) in an enamelled frame shows the perfection to which portrait cutting in stone and the art of the goldsmith could be carried. ❧ Cellini, together with the Milanese medallist Cristoforo Caradosso Foppa (ac. 1475-1527) who in 1505 settled in Rome, did much to improve the process of striking medals. ε❧ In Milan during the Cinquecento, Leone Leoni (1509-90), whose life was as turbulent as that of his rival Cellini, was the most important medallist. Another Milanese, Jacopo Nizzola da Trezzo (1515/20-89), worked in a style which much resembled Leoni's. The medal of Gianello della Torro (no. 67), for example, has variously been attributed to Leoni and Da Trezzo. Leoni appears to have fought violently with Gianello, calling him an ox in human shape; yet he probably authored the medal. ε❧ Quite a number of Cinquecento medallists, like Valerio Belli (1468-1546), Giovanni Bernardi da Castelbolognese (1496-c. 1555), and Alessandro Cesati, called Il Grecchetto (ac. 1538-53), also practised gem engraving, and their style sometimes betrays a hand more accustomed to working in hard materials. Cesati has been credited with some important advances in die-sinking, and Michelangelo expressed a high opinion of Cesati's work. ε❧ A very special branch of medallic art developed when the wax model, hitherto just a means for producing the medal, itself became the final work of art. Pastorino de' Pastorini (1508-92), Antonio Abondio (1538-91) as well as his son Alessandro (c. 1570-1648, ac. 1595-1640) were among the major creators in this medium and produced some wax portraits which can hold their own with the best miniatures of that period. Some of these waxes are polychromed, and in their style they demonstrate a trend in sixteenth-century art toward more elaborate detail. ε❧ During the seventeenth century and beyond, the art of making medals in Italy remained rather stationary. However, some artists of distinction still flourished. Among these were Gaspare Mola (c. 1580-c. 1640), who worked for the Savoy and Medici families (no. 43); the Hameranis, who were Papal medallists for almost two hundred years; as well as the Travanis, Girolamo Lucenti (ac. c. 1668-90), and a number of others. ε❧ In France, medallic art goes back to the close of the Middle Ages, and includes that group of medals, already cited, made by Flemish-Burgundian goldsmiths in the late fourteenth century. Between 1451 and 1460 another series of medals commemorating historic events was produced; most of these had long chronogrammic inscriptions, commemorating the expulsion of the English from France at the end of the Hundred Years' War. But these pieces were entirely the work of coin engravers and were struck from dies, based on designs borrowed from contemporary coins. ε❧ During the reign of Charles VIII (born 1470, King 1483-98), the French portrait medal proper came into being. From that period date pieces presented by cities to the kings and queens of France on the occasions of their royal visits. A noteworthy example is a medal presented to Anne of Brittany (born 1477, Queen 1491-1514) in March, 1494, upon her state entry into the city of Lyon accompanied by her husband, Charles VIII, who was on his way to the Italian campaign; the medal depicts a golden lion holding a cup containing a hundred gold medals. Another example of such homage medals is the one offered to Anne at a later visit to Lyon, in March, 1500, this time accompanied by her second husband, Louis XII (born 1462, King 1498-1515) (no. 78). ε❧ While the style of the earlier medals had been that of the late Middle Ages, by this time Italian medallists, notably Niccolo di Forzore Spinelli and Giovanni Candida (c. 1450-c. 1494), were employed at the Burgundian Court of Charles the Bold, where they introduced the style of the Italian Renaissance. ε❧ Francis I (born 1494, King 1515-47), the first Renaissance man on the French throne, had a great passion for Italian art and attracted to his court many of its artists, among them Benvenuto Cellini, as well as such lesser known artists as

Matteo dal Nassaro (1515-c. 1547) and Benedetto Ramelli (ac. c. 1530-37). Henry II (born 1519, King 1547-59), on the other hand, patronized native-born engravers; it was during his reign that the Monnaie du Moulin opened and the French die-cutter Etienne de Laune was appointed (1552) to it. ⁊ The most remarkable series of French medals of the second half of the sixteenth century are the Valois medallions; their author was the sculptor Germain Pilon (c. 1535-90), who in 1572 became Controller-General of the French mint. These large cast medallions, some of which measure as much as 171 mm. in diameter, made between 1573 and 1577, chiefly depict royalty such as Henry II, Catherine de Medici, Charles IX, Elizabeth of Austria, Henry III (no. 80), etc. ⁊ In the first half of the seventeenth century France ranked first in medallic art. The greatest medallist of the period was Guillaume Dupré (c. 1574-c. 1643). The sixty or more medals executed by him display an elegant style and superb technical skill. Although nearly all his medals were cast, their surface texture is so fine that it is easy to mistake them for struck pieces. A number of other French medallists added luster to the seventeenth century, among whom were Jean Warin (ac. 1627-c. 1672) and Claude Warin (ac. c. 1630-54). The former probably was second only to Dupré. To Claude have been attributed some charming portraits of English subjects from the period of Charles I (born 1600, King 1625-49). After the seventeenth century French medallic art declined before it reached some prominence again during the Empire in the early nineteenth century. ⁊ In Germany the development of medallic art started with Hans Schwarz (born 1492, ac. 1516-c. 1530). The two most prominent centers were Nürnberg, the home of goldsmithry, and Augsburg, where metal casting was prevalent. Leipzig also deserves mention. ⁊ As Florence had its Lorenzo de' Medici (1449-92), so did the Germanic lands have an art-loving Emperor, Maximilian I (born 1459, Emperor 1493-1519), whose patronage of die-engravers and bronze casters, even while a young archduke, greatly contributed to furthering this branch of the fine arts. As early as 1477, Maximilian had himself portrayed on a medal by Giovanni Candida (no. 27), together with his young bride, the beautiful Mary of Burgundy. ⁊ While wax served as the material for the models of Italian medals, the models for the early German medals were carved in boxwood, honestone, or slate; alabaster and mother-of-pearl were also occasionally used. From these wood and stone models, through the intermediary of a negative mold, the medals were cast, and then in many cases subsequently chased by the artists, who brought to them all the meticulousness of detail so much admired in German Renaissance medals. While Italian artists frequently signed their medals (during the early period their name preceded by the proud OPVS), German medallists usually left their works unsigned or simply used initials. The models were cut either directly from life—as some scholars believe the inscription "imago ad vivam effigiem expressa" on a medal of Erasmus indicates—or, as was more usual, after portrait sketches. The Augsburg medallist Hans Schwarz appears to have worked mainly from sketches, 136 of which have been preserved. ⁊ The boxwood model was used chiefly in Augsburg, Ulm, and the Allgäu; its masters were Hans Schwarz, Martin Schaffner (ac. c. 1522-30), Christoph Weiditz (ac. 1523-c. 1533), Friedrich Hagenauer (ac. 1525-46), Hans Kels (ac. 1527-c. 1554), and his younger brother Veit Kels (ac. 1536). Their work encompasses the period of the boxwood model. In Nürnberg the stone model was predominant due chiefly to the work of Matthes Gebel (ac. c. 1526-c. 1555) and Joachim Deschler (ac. 1540-c. 1569). ⁊ The extent to which Albrecht Dürer (1471-1528) played a part in the history of the German medal has long been a subject of controversy. There is, however, general agreement and, in one case at least, also documentary evidence that several medals and plaquettes, even if not executed by his own hand, certainly were made after his designs (see, for example, no. 184). ᛊ᠎ After the middle of the sixteenth century, wax replaced stone and wood as modelling material. This technique was introduced into Germany chiefly by Antonio Abondio, an Italian artist from Lombardy, who came into the employ of the Hapsburgs. ᛊ᠎ Much of the merit of the German Renaissance medal is to be found in its perfect technical execution. Some of the early productions are marvels of delicacy and minuteness, with their life-like portraits and skillfully designed heraldic reverses. The portrait, to which the Italian medallist lent refinement and ideality, was modelled more realistically by his German counterpart whose style did not conceal the sitter's possible lack of dignified appearance. Faithfulness to reality was his goal, and he succeeded to an unprecedented degree. Thus we sometimes can see, and be amused by, the unflattering pictorial record of many a petty ruler, city councilman, church sexton, or butter dealer, who considered himself a suitable subject for portrayal on a medal (see, for example, no. 90). There probably is no other medallic school which has left us such accurate likenesses. ᛊ᠎ After the great age of the German medal had lasted for about half a century—taking the Augsburg Diet of 1518 with its first medals by Hans Schwarz as the starting point—it began to decline. Gradually the cast medal was eclipsed by the hammer-struck medal. Portraiture no longer was fired by the same vitality and individuality so typical of earlier medals. At about the middle of the sixteenth century a development in technique took place which was to have a profound impact on medallic art: the invention of the mechanical coin press at Augsburg. It presented the art of the medal with new potentialities, permitting a considerable increase in production. ᛊ᠎ Highly esteemed during the seventeenth century were die-cutters such as Sebastian Dadler (ac. 1619-54), Johann Hoehn (c. 1637-93), Philipp Heinrich Mueller (1654-1719), and a number of others, some of whom were also influenced by the simultaneously developing Dutch school. In the almost microscopic detail of their medals unfold historic events—battles, peace treaties, coronations, and weddings. The sumptuous taste of the Baroque is expressed in their elaborate and ornamental designs. ᛊ᠎ At the beginning of the sixteenth century several medallists of note made their appearance in the Low Countries. These include Quentin Metsys (1460-1530), the blacksmith turned painter and medallist, maker of a magnificent portrait medal of Erasmus; Jean Second (1511-36), who modelled in stone, wood, or wax with equal skill; and Michael Mercator (1491-1539) of Venlo. The latter was in the service of Floris of Egmont, Count of Buren, in the dual capacity of artist and diplomat. In 1527 Mercator was at work in England, where he portrayed Henry VIII. ᛊ᠎ There were other medallists like Jacob Jonghelinck (1531-1606) of Antwerp, probably one of the best known representatives of the school, who also met with great success as a sculptor, seal-engraver, and goldsmith. Also prominent was the medallist Conrad Bloc (ac. 1575-1602), who was active in The Netherlands as well as in France and Germany. ᛊ᠎ Yet with few exceptions the medallists working in the Low Countries during the sixteenth century were hesitant to assert themselves in an independent native style; their works usually show strong foreign influence. In the case of Jonghelinck, it is the Milanese; in the case of Mercator and Bloc, the German schools. A well-defined Dutch medallic school did not emerge until the seventeenth century. Its chief masters were Pieter van Abeele (ac. 1622-77), Jan Filius Lutma (c. 1605-85), and O. Wouter Muller (ac. 1653-88), all skilled in the characteristically Dutch repoussé medal. In this process the obverse and reverse of the medal were separately formed by being hammered or pressed into relief, and then the two shells were joined together by a rim. In addition, Jurriaan Pool (ac. mid-seventeenth century) and Jan Roettiers (1631-1703), whose descendants and relatives became coin and medal engravers in The Netherlands, England, and France, contributed significantly to the development of the struck medal. ❧ The plaquette is closely allied to the medal from which, however, it differs in various respects; most obviously in shape, subject, and (with a few exceptions) the absence of a reverse design. The shape of a plaquette may be square, oblong, oval, circular, shield-like, etc. Subjects include religious, mythological, allegorical, and historical scenes, as well as themes based on Greek and Roman art or classical literature. Since one of the principal features of most medals is its portrait, some likenesses of contemporary persons on bronzes which, though uniface, have shapes other than round, are classified as medals (nos. 2, 7, 8, and 29, for example); although others (nos. 180 and 181) are listed among the plaquettes. On the other hand, certain small round uniface bronzes of figures from the Roman world are regarded as plaquettes (see nos. 176-179). ❧ In the main, the plaquette was an object of art to be enjoyed for its aesthetic appeal and artistic qualities. In their practical application, plaquettes served as decorations on functional or religious objects; those with suitable representations were occasionally used as a pax, a tablet to be kissed during mass. By far the greater number of plaquettes were cast by the lost wax process described previously. ❧ Italy, the birthplace of the Renaissance medal, likewise was the cradle of the plaquette, and from there the art spread beyond the Alps to France, Flanders, and Germany. The development of the plaquette began about the middle of the fifteenth century, parallel to that of the medal, and flourished well into the sixteenth century. ❧ The creators of plaquettes often were the same men who figured prominently in the art of the medal. Gianfrancesco Enzola of Parma, Cristoforo Caradosso Foppa of Milan, Fra Antonio da Brescia (ac. 1487-1513), and others were skilled in both crafts. Valerio Belli, Giovanni Bernardi da Castelbolognese, though primarily engravers of crystal and precious stones, produced a considerable number of medals and plaquettes as well. ❧ Unfortunately, many of the plaquette artists have remained anonymous, although at times stylistic comparison with medals or other works of art permits at least a geographical attribution. In the past, a number of plaquettes have been ascribed to the Florentine sculptor Donatello (c. 1386-1466); an example is a Pietà (no. 156), more recently given to another Florentine master, Agostino di Duccio (1418-98). ❧ Among the more prolific artists involved in this field during the late fifteenth and early sixteenth centuries was the Paduan Andrea Briosco (1470-1532), called Riccio ("Curly Haired"). It is believed that he may also have been the author of plaquettes bearing the signature Ulocrino (Greek for "Curly Haired"). Another prominent figure was Jacopo Sansovino (1486-1570), a Florentine by birth, who first was active in Rome but settled about 1527 in Venice, which already had a long tradition in bronze casting. Here the prosperous Venetian merchants vied with each other in building opulent palaces, among whose furnishings were collections of bronze statuettes, plaquettes, and medals. Sansovino's favorite subjects for plaquettes were scenes from the New Testament. For St. Mark's, Sansovino did the door of the sacristy, the six reliefs in the choir, the Four Evangelists on the balustrade of the choir, and a number of other figures. ❧ In conclusion it may be said that the art of the medal and plaquette complements many of the major arts of the Renaissance. These objects, by virtue of their small size, have withstood the vicissitudes of time, and have played an important role in contributing to our understanding of the Renaissance and Baroque periods. ❧ In the present catalogue, the arrangement of the Italian medals up to the time of Benvenuto Cellini follows the order of G. F. Hill, *Corpus of Italian Medals of the Renaissance before Cellini*. German medals of the sixteenth century have been grouped according to the order established by G. Habich, *Die Deutschen Schaumunzen des XVI. Jahrhunderts.* ❧ Our thanks are due to Mr. Marvin S. Sadik, Director of the Bowdoin College Museum of Art, whose enthusiasm for medals and plaquettes first sparked the idea of this exhibition. He most generously gave of his time and wide knowledge and also shouldered the burden of preparing this catalogue, which it is hoped will be of interest to old friends of the medal and plaquette and will help to introduce others to this fascinating field.

L. S.

All medals and plaquettes have been reproduced
to exact size. Bibliography and indexes
follow the catalogue.

ITALIAN MEDALS TO THE TIME OF BENVENUTO CELLINI

ANTONIO PISANO called PISANELLO c. 1397-c. 1455

Medallist from 1438-49

Antonio Pisano was probably born at Pisa about 1397. In his younger years he moved to Verona, where he was surnamed "Pisanello" (Little man from Pisa). He already was a highly distinguished painter of frescoes, portraits, and animals before 1438 when his first medal, marking the beginning of Renaissance medallic art, was executed.

In the history of art, Pisanello ranks as the founder of the cast medal and, indeed, as the most celebrated of all medallists; but he never forgot that he was a painter, and he signs his medals OPVS PISANO PICTORIS (the work of Pisano the painter).

His medals reveal the trained eye of the painter in the clear and subtle lines of the portraits; they combine realistic rendering, sometimes extraordinarily severe, with dignity of character. The reverses show a keen observation of nature and a marked liking for rocky landscapes and animals (see the reverses of nos. 1 and 4).

The last medallic creations of this great master date from the year 1449; he died c. 1455. (For a portrait of Pisanello see no. 6 by Marescotti.)

1

Filippo Maria Visconti 1392-1447, Duke of Milan 1412-47

Bronze medal, 100 mm. diam., c. 1441

PHILIPPVSMARIA · ANGLVS · DVX · MEDIOLANI · ETCETERA · PAPIE · ANGLERIE · QVE · COMES · AC · GENVE · DOMINVS · (The Duke lost Genoa in 1435, but kept his title.) Bust right, wearing cap with edge turned up all around and soft crown. Brocaded dress. Plain linear border.

Rev. OPVS · PISANI · PICTORIS on a sunken band, below. Mountainous landscape with tops of buildings on one of which is a colossal female statue holding sceptre. In the foreground, three horsemen. The Duke to left in full armor with biscione crest to helmet, lance erect, horse prancing; on right, small page on horseback much foreshortened from behind; between them armed horseman to front. Plain linear border enclosing upper part of design.

Hill, *Corpus*, no. 21, pl. 4
Armand, I, 8, 23
Heiss, *Pisano*, II, 2; pl. I, 2

Hill, *Pisanello*, pp. 125 ff.
Habich, pl. II, 1
Tresor, Pisano, pl. I, 3
Friedlaender, p. 36, 17
Rizzini, no. 20
Supino, pl. VIII, 17
Venice, *Correr Museum*, no. 18

The dragon on the Duke's helmet appears in the coat of arms of the Viscontis.

Provenance: Count Trivulzio Coll.

2

Francesco I Sforza 1401-66, Duke of Milan 1450-66

Octagonal bronze medal, H. 82 mm., W. 49 mm., c. 1441

Bust left, wearing tall cap with soft round crown and edge turned up all around; plate armor over shirt of mail.

No reverse.

cf. the following:
Hill, *Corpus*, no. 23, pl. 4
Armand, I, 8, 22
Heiss, *Pisano*, p. 15, 3; pl. II, 1
Hill, *Pisanello*, p. 127, pl. 32
Habich, pl. II, 3

3

3

Lionello d'Este 1407-50, Lord of Ferrara 1441-50

Bronze medal, 69 mm. diam.

LEONELLVS MARCHIO ESTENSIS (words separated by olive branches). Bust right, with short curly hair, wearing surcoat with scale decoration over mail.

Rev. · OPVS · PISANI · PICTORIS A mast with inflated sail; at its foot, on left, a nude old man seated facing right; on right, a nude young man seated facing left, seen from behind.

Hill, *Corpus,* no. 25
Armand, I, 3, 5
Heiss, *Pisano,* p. 19, 6; pl. III, 1
Friedlaender, p. 34, 10

The mast with the sail is the Este impresa known as the Vela.

4

Lionello d'Este

Bronze medal, 100 mm. diam., 1444

LEONELLVS · MARCHIO | · ESTENSIS · in two lines across field; above, · GE · R · AR · ; below, · D · FERRARIE · REGII · ET · MV-TINE · Bust left, with short curly hair, wearing richly brocaded dress.
Rev. · OPVS · | PISANI · | PICTORIS · Above, on rocky ground, a lion standing right, singing from a scroll of music held by nude Cupid left;

in background, tall square pillar on which is a mast with inflated sail and · M · | CCCC | XLIIII; in left background, on rocky hill, eagle seen from behind, perched on leafless tree.

Hill, *Corpus,* no. 32, pl. 6
Armand, I, 3, 8
Heiss, *Pisano,* p. 19, 11; pl. IV, 2
Hill, *Pisanello,* pp. 148 ff., pl. 39
Habich, pl. III, 1
Friedlaender, p. 34, 12; pl. IV
Supino, no. 5
British Museum, *Select Italian Medals,* pl. 5
British Museum, *Guide,* p. 10, fig. 3

The reverse, Amor teaching the lion (Lionello) to sing is one of the most humorous and one of the finest of Pisano's compositions. The medal with its poetic charm commemorates the marriage of Lionello with Maria of Aragon, the natural daughter of Alfonso of Naples (April 1444); Lionello is called GE(ner) R(egis) AR(agonum). The eagle probably is the eagle of the Este arms. Musical pomps were a leading feature of the marriage ceremony.

Provenance: Dr. Benno Geiger Coll.

ANTONIO MARESCOTTI ac. 1444-62

Little is known about Marescotti's life. It is believed, although not proven, that he was a sculptor as well as a medallist. A terra-cotta bust of Giovanni Tavelli of Tossignano, Bishop of Ferrara, who died in 1446, in the vestibule of the Hospital of St. Anne at Ferrara, is generally attributed to him. (For a portrait of Tavelli, see no. 5.)

5

Beato Giovanni Tavelli da Tossignano 1386-1446, Bishop of Ferrara 1431-46

Bronze medal, 89.5 mm. diam., 1446

DEVOTISSIMVS · PAVPER · PR · D · IOHANES · EPS · FERRA-RIENM Bust left, tonsured, with rays issuing from crown of head, wearing cloak. In front, mitre.

Rev. EGO · SICVT · OLIVA · FRVCTIFICAVI · SVAVITATE · ODO · I · DO DI In field left, MCCCC | XLVI · In field right, MARE | SCO-TVS | - F - The Bishop, in loose undergarment, kneeling left in adoration, rays pouring on him from heaven; an olive tree sprouting from his head; in front of him, his shoes; behind him, his cloak.

Hill, *Corpus,* no. 79, pl. 18
Brescia (Brozzoni Coll.), (illustrated in Hill, *Corpus*)
Armand, I, 29, 8

Oppenheimer, no. 13, now in Morgenroth Coll.
Heiss, *Niccolo,* p. 22, 1; pl. II, 1
Koehler, XIX, p. 73
Habich, pl. XVII, 4
Friedlaender, p. 54, 1; pl. X
Mazzuchelli, I, IX, 3
Rizzini, no. 55
British Museum, *Select Italian Medals,* pl. 13, 1
British Museum, *Guide,* p. 13, fig. 9
The halo does not imply an official beatification, but is an anticipation; the medal must have been made immediately after the Bishop's death. He is described as Blessed in a biography written before 1501 (Gruyer, I, p. 261).

6

Antonio Pisano called *Pisanello* c. 1397-c. 1455
Bronze medal, 57 mm. diam., c. 1440-43
· PISANVS · PICTOR. Bust left, wearing brocaded dress and high, soft, crumpled beretta.

Rev. · F · S · K · I · (spray) · P · F · T · (spray) in conventional laurel wreath with spray rising from bottom.
Hill, *Corpus,* no. 87, pl. 20
Armand, I, 9, 25
Tresor, I, 1, 1
Habich, pl. XI, 4
Friedlaender, p. 41, 27; pl. I
Rizzini, 22
Supino, 19, pl. IX
Hill, *PMIA,* p. 31, 5; pl. XVIII
British Museum, *Select Italian Medals,* pl. 13, 2
Heiss, *Pisano,* p. 9
Ferrer, IV, 573 (attributed to Pisanello), this specimen
G. F. Hill reads the initials on the reverse as meaning the seven virtues: Fides, Spes, Karitas, Iustitia, Prudentia, Fortitudo, Temperantia.
Provenance: Loebbecke Coll., Munich 1908, no. 3, pl. 1, also illustrated on the cover of the catalogue.

FERRARESE OR OTHER NORTH ITALIAN ARTISTS, 1470-1500

7

Unknown Man
Rectangular bronze medal, H. 79.5 mm., W. 57.5 mm.
Male bust left, wearing conical hat and robe with pleated front.
No reverse.
cf. Hill, *Corpus,* no. 126 (69 x 48 mm.)
Provenance: Luccardi Coll., pl. 42, no. 13

8

Unknown Boy
Rectangular bronze medal, H. 66.5 mm., W. 53.5 mm.
Bust left, with long hair, wearing round cap; bust loosely draped.

No reverse.
Hill, *Corpus,* no. 140, pl. 27 (46 x 38 mm.)
Hill, *Dreyfus Coll.,* pl. XIV, 47
Provenance: Luccardi Coll., pl. 42, no. 12

FERRARESE c. 1500-30

9

Opizo Remo Ducal Secretary to Alfonso I 1505-34
Bronze medal, 68 mm. diam.
OPIZO · REMVS · ALFON · ESTEN · DV · III · SECRETA Bust left with bobbed hair, wearing cap with back flap turned up, and gown buttoned in front. Below, a fig branch. Very high relief.

Rev. Jason and the dragon (from Fra Antonio da Brescia's plaquette).
Hill, *Corpus,* no. 156, pl. 29
Armand, ii, 92, 15
Rev. De Ricci, *Dreyfus Coll.,* no. 116, pl. xxxiv
Loebbecke Coll., Munich 1908, no. 26, pl. v (chased)
Provenance: Dr. Benno Geiger Coll.

MATTEO DE' PASTI (Matteo di Maestro Andrea de' Pasti) ac. 1441-68

This accomplished Veronese architect, sculptor, painter, miniaturist, and medallist is first heard of in 1441 at Venice, where he worked for Piero di Cosimo de' Medici. In 1446 he settled in Rimini, soon becoming persona grata at the court of Sigismondo Malatesta. In 1454 he is referred to as "noble."

De' Pasti's medals of Sigismondo were made between 1446 and 1450. The castle of Rimini on the reverse ranks as one of the finest representations of a building on any medal. De' Pasti's versatility and reputation as an artist were enormous; it may be said that, as a medallist, he took up the mantle of Pisanello.

10

Sigismondo Pandolfo Malatesta 1417-68, Lord of Rimini 1432-68
Bronze medal, 83.5 mm. diam., 1446
(rosette) SIGISMONDVS · PANDVLFVS · DE · MALATESTIS · S · RO · ECLESIE · C · GENERALIS Bust left, wearing cuirass and surcoat. The abbreviations stand for: SACRAE ROMANAE ECCLESIAE CAPITANVS GENERALIS.

Rev. (rosette) CASTELLVM · SISMONDVM · ARIMINENSE · M · CCCC · XLVI The castle of Rimini.

Hill, *Corpus,* no. 174, pl. 33 (London)
Numismatic Chronicle (1917), p. 308, no. 14
Heiss, *Alberti, etc.,* p. 31, 10; pl. v, 3
Fabriczy, pl. ix
Supino, no. 28
Hill, *Pisanello,* pl. 66
British Museum, *Select Italian Medals,* pl. 11, 1
Calabi & Cornaggia, p. 95
Rimini Castle, the "Rocca Malatestiana," begun in 1438, was finished in 1446. This reverse is copied in Piero dei Franceschi's fresco of Sigismondo kneeling before his patron saint in San Francesco, Rimini.
Provenance: Luccardi Coll.

11

Sigismondo Pandolfo Malatesta
Bronze medal, 82 mm. diam., 1446
Obverse same as in preceding number.
Rev. Fortitude, crowned, cuirassed, and in long tunic, seated facing front in a meadow on a throne, the sides of which are formed by foreparts of elephants. She holds in both hands a broken column. Below: (rosette) M · CCCC · XLVI (rosette).
Hill, *Corpus,* no. 179, pl. 33 (no. 174 obverse, no. 178 reverse)
Armand, i, 20, 10
Tresor, ii, pl. iii, 1
Numismatic Chronicle (1917), p. 309, no. 18
Rizzini, no. 35
Metzler, no. 6, pl. iii
Calabi & Cornaggia, p. 39, no. 6 (London, George III) and p. 97
Hill, *Dreyfus Coll.,* no. 61 (same reverse), pl. xviii
Heiss, *Alberti, etc.,* p. 31, no. 11; pl. vi, 1

12

Sigismondo Pandolfo Malatesta
Bronze medal, 32 mm. diam., 1447
SIGISMVNDVS PANDVLFVS · MALATESTA · Bust left, wearing mail and surcoat.
Rev. PONTIFICII · EXERCITVS · IMP · M. CCCCXLVII. An arm, issuing from a cloud, and holding a birch rod.
Hill, *Corpus,* no. 182, pl. 34
The birch rod is the symbol of command.

13

Sigismondo Pandolfo Malatesta

Bronze medal, 80 mm. diam., 1446

SIGISMVNDVS PANDVLFVS · MALATESTA · PAN · F · Bust left, wearing plate armor over mail shirt.

Rev. CASTELLVM · SISMVNDVM · ARIMINENSE · M · CCCC · XLVI · The castle of Rimini.

Hill, *Corpus,* no. 184, pl. 34
Armand, I, 20, 12
Numismatic Chronicle (1917), p. 307, 12
Calabi & Cornaggia, p. 42, 12
Provenance: Dr. Benno Geiger Coll.

MANTUAN in the manner of PIERO JACOPO DI ANTONIO ALARI BUONACOLSI called L'ANTICO c. 1460-c. 1528

14

Giulia Astallia

Bronze medal, 63 mm. diam., c. 1485

DIVA · IVLIA ASTALLIA Half-figure of girl left, head bent a little forward, hair in long braid knotted up and tied with fillet, bodice laced in front, neck open.

Rev. EXEMPLVM VNICVM · FOR · ET · PVD · Phoenix on burning pyre, looking up at the sun's rays issuing from a cloud.

Hill, *Corpus,* no. 218
Armand, I, 83.3
Habich, pl. LV, 1
Bode, *Zeitschrift,* p. 37
British Museum, *Guide,* p. 16, fig. 13
Arethuse I (1923/4), p. 17, pl. III, 2
Friedlaender, p. 129
Fabriczy, p. 49
Supino, no. 96
Simon, no. 123
Archivo Storico dell'Arte III (1890), p. 31
British Museum, *Select Italian Medals,* pl. 19, 5
Hill, *Medals of the Renaissance,* pl. VII, 2
British Museum, *Guide,* p. 16, fig. 13
Burlington Magazine XX (Oct. 1911), p. 23, pl. II, F
Revue Numismatique (1892), pp. 485 ff.
Tresor, II, pl. XLI, 6
Weimar, *Goethe-Sammlung,* no. 186

Giulia Astallia is generally identified with Giulia of Gazzuolo, heroine of Matteo Bandello's Nov. I, 8, who, having been violated by a servant of Bishop Lodovico of Mantua (1483-1510), drowned herself; the Bishop had a statue erected to her.

MANTUAN close to GIANCRISTOFORO ROMANO d. 1512

15

Lucrezia Borgia 1480-1519

Bronze medal, 59.5 mm. diam., c. 1505

LVCRETIA (leaf) BORGIA (leaf) ESTEN · FERRARIAE (leaf) MVT · AC · REGII · D · Bust left, in high relief, heavy hair covering temples and neck, with a braid drawn from temples across and knotted behind, at shoulders tied together in a pigtail, beginning of which is seen; low dress fastened on left shoulder with ring; double cord with pendant on breast; straight truncation.

Rev. VIRTVTI · AC · FORMAE · PVDICITIA · PRAECIOSISSIMVM (two leaves on stalk). Nude Amor, blindfolded, tied with hands behind his back to a laurel tree, on which are suspended on left a broken quiver; on right, a trophy-like arrangement of a tablet inscribed BO | FPHFF | EN, a violin and its bow placed like a psaltery, a bundle of sheets of music, and a bow with broken string.

Hill, *Corpus,* no. 233
Armand, I, 118, 3
Foville, *Gazette des Beaux Arts,* 39 (1908), p. 387

Friedlaender, *Berliner Blaetter* III (1866), pp. 202-207, pl. XXXV (attributed to Filippino Lippi)
Bode, *Zeitschrift,* p. 37
Habich, pl. LXIV, 4
Arethuse I (1923/4), p. 19, pl. III, 4
Nanni, 1902

In 1503 Lucrezia wrote to Bembo asking him to suggest a motto for this medal. The lettering on the tablet has been analyzed by Friedlaender: "Filippinus PHilippi Filius Fecit EN BOnonia"; by Milanesi (Bibl. Com. Siena): "Bona Franciscus Panini Hoc fecit Ferrariae ENcenia" or "Francesco Panini Horafo Ferrarese Fece."

Provenance: Elkan Coll. 1934, no. 21 (as "Maître a l'Amour captif")

GIANFRANCESCO ENZOLA Parma ac. 1456-78

Enzola worked chiefly at Parma and Ferrara. His early medals are on a small scale, and for a while he tried to strike his medals instead of casting them, but the struck products never attained the fineness of his cast ones, especially in the portraits.

Among the artist's various employers was Francesco Sforza, whom Enzola portrayed on several medals, the earliest bearing his signature (see the following number).

16

Francesco I Sforza 1401-66, Duke of Milan 1450-66

Bronze medal, 42.5 mm. diam., 1456

(Biscione) FR · SFORTIA VICECOMES · MLI · DVX IIII BELLI PATER · ET · PACIS · AVTOR · M · CCCC LVI · Bust right, elderly, in shirt of mail under plate; across field · V · F · Pearled border.

Rev. Artist's signature: IO · FR · ENZOLAE · · PARMENSIS · OPVS · On rocky ground, a greyhound seated left under a fruit tree; a hand issuing from a radiant cloud touches him; below him, on the ground, a bridle attached by a chain to the tree. Pearled border.

Hill, *Corpus,* no. 281, pl. 45
Armand, I, 44, 6
Roville, p. 205
Habich, pl. LVII, 5
Friedlaender, p. 115, 1; pl. XXI
Simon, no. 128
Rizzini, no. 71
Supino, no. 51
Litta, *Sforza,* pl. II, 3

The reverse shows the Duke's impresa (motto: Quietum nemo me impune lacesset); cf. Paolo Giovio, *Dialogo dell'Imprese* (Lyon 1574), p. 41; Friedlaender, p. 116.

SPERANDIO OF MANTUA ac. 1466-1504

Probably born in Mantua about 1425, Sperandio moved at an early age to Ferrara, but always remained proud of his Mantuan citizenship. His fame spread over the entire north of Italy as a goldsmith, sculptor, architect, medallist, and cannon-founder. He was mainly active in Ferrara, Faenza, and Bologna.

By 1504, Sperandio became too feeble to continue his work, and a year later he died in Venice, where he had been active as a cannon-founder.

Sperandio's style is characterized by vigorous portraiture. Goethe was especially fond of his works and ranked him first among the Italian medallists.

17

Fra Cesario Contughi of Ferrara

Bronze medal, 84 mm. diam., First Ferrarese period (1462-77)

FR · CESARIVS · FER · ORDINS · SER · B · M · V(rose)DIVIN · L · T · EXELLEN · DOC · AC DIVI · VER · FAMOSIS · PREDICA-TOR · Elderly bust left, wearing habit with hood over head.

Rev. · INSPICE · MORTALE · GENVS · MORS · OMNIA · DELET · and in arc below: OPVS · SPERANDEI Fra Cesario, wearing long tunic, and scapular with hood over his head, seated on rock three-quarters right, resting head on left hand, and contemplating a death's head on the ground to right.

Hill, *Corpus*, no. 363, pl. 61
Armand, I, 67, 16
Heiss, *Sperandio*, p. 36, no. 16
Foville, p. 40, 6 (assigned to 1467)
Gruyer, p. 640
Weber, pp. 531-532

GIOVANNI (ZUAN) BOLDÙ (Giovanni di Pasqualino Boldù) ac. 1454-c. 1477

Although Boldù describes himself on his medals as a painter, nothing is definitely known of his paintings. He may, however, have worked in Venice, both as a painter and as a medallist.

Boldù had a special affection for classical subjects, and in the case of the Caracalla medal (see the following number), the obverse, except for minor alterations, is directly taken from a Roman coin. He doubtless was one of the most important Venetian medallists.

18

Emperor Caracalla 211-17

Bronze medal, 90.4 mm. diam., 1466

· ANTONINVS · PIVS · AVGVSTVS · Laureate and draped bust of the youthful Caracalla facing left.

Rev. · IO · SON · FINE · in an arc above. Below, in a sunken arc, · M · CCCC · LXVI · The youthful artist Boldù seated on a rock. To the right the winged genius of death, seated on the ground, holding a flame (symbol of the soul) in his left hand and resting his right elbow on a human skull. Pearled border over upper part of design.

Hill, *Corpus*, no. 423, pl. 80
Armand, I, 37, 4
Weber, p. 530
Heiss, *Venetian Medals*, p. 107, pl. II, 3
Spitzer Coll., no. 1335, pl. II, 35 (now Paris)
Loebbecke Coll., Munich 1908, no. 10, pl. III
Friedlaender, p. 89, 7; pl. XIV
Supino, 48
British Museum, *Select Italian Medals*, pl. XII, 1
British Museum, *Guide*, p. 19, fig. 18
Revue Numismatique (1895), p. 567

This medal is generally attributed to Boldù, based upon the fact that the reverse composition is identical with that of Hill, *Corpus*, no. 421. There is no resemblance in lettering; in addition, the style of the obverse is broader than is usual with Boldù. The head of Caracalla is taken from a Roman aureus, cf. Cohen 96, in which the Emperor is facing right. The little genius on the reverse is after a design by Pietro da Fano.

Provenance: Count Trivulzio Coll.

VETTOR DI ANTONIO GAMBELLO called CAMELIO 1455/60-1537

Camelio worked as engraver to the Venetian mint from 1484 to 1523, but probably was active as a medallist at an earlier stage. He also experimented with struck medals, but his cast pieces are doubtless the finer ones. The two medals of Gentile Bellini and his brother Giovanni are among Camelio's most beautiful creations. He died in Rome, where he was employed as Superintendent of the Papal mint. During his last decade he did very little work.

19

Giovanni Bellini c. 1430-1516

Bronze medal, 58 mm. diam., c. 1495

IOANNES BELLINVS · VENET · PICTOR · OP · Bust left, with long hair, plain cap, dress with stole over right shoulder. Pearled border.

Rev. Owl perched left on fragment of a branch; above, VIRTVTIS ET INGENII; below, VICTOR CAMELIVS | FACIEBAT · Pearled border.

Hill, *Corpus*, no. 438, pl. 83
Armand, I, 115, 2
Habich, p. 94
Fabriczy, p. 78, pl. XVI, I
Hill, *Dreyfus Coll.*, p. 12, no. XII
Heiss, *Venetian Medals*, p. 123, pl. VII, 2
Friedlaender, p. 95, no. 4; pl. XVII
Hill, *PMIA*, p. 39, 14; pl. XX

The last two words of the obverse legend stand for PICTORVM OPTIMVS.

Provenance: Count Trivulzio Coll.

VENETIAN, EARLY SIXTEENTH CENTURY

20

Fra Giovanni Cornaro Venetian Benedictine of the Abbey of Praglia, Abbot of Santa Giustina of Padua 1507-14

Bronze medal, 44 mm. diam.

IO · CORNELIVS · MONA COR · CASIN · COLVMEN Aged bust left, tonsured and almost entirely bald, wearing Benedictine habit with small hood.

Rev. PIETAS EVANGELICA A shepherd standing three-quarters left, looking to front; he carries crook in right hand, and a sheep on his shoulders, and drives a flock of sheep past a palm tree on which is a pelican.

Hill, *Corpus*, no. 527, pl. 96
Armand, II, 70, 5
Habich, pl. LXVIII, 8
Simon, no. 285
Rizzini, no. 495
Heiss, *Venetian Medals*, p. 180, pl. XII, 7
Keary, no. 73
British Museum, *Select Italian Medals*, pl. 38, 5
Loehr, no. 311, pl. XXVII
Hill, *Dreyfus Coll.*, no. 168, pl. XLIII

FRANCESCO RAIBOLINI called IL FRANCIA c. 1450-c. 1517

From about 1508 until his death Francia was in control of the Bolognese mint, working for Julius II, after the Pope had taken the city from Giovanni II Bentivoglio in 1506. Prior to that, according to Vasari, Francia cut dies for the Bentivoglio, who in 1494 had been granted the right of coinage by Emperor Maximilian. Francia was also a goldsmith and painter.

The following medal has been attributed to Francia.

21

Giovanni II Bentivoglio 1462-1506, Duke of Bologna 1494-1506

Bronze medal, 28 mm. diam., 1494

IOANNES · BENTIVOLVS II · BONONIENSIS · Bust right, with long hair, parted to show the ear, wearing low cap with back flap turned up; doublet and coat with open collar. Pearled border.

Rev. (in six lines) · MAXIMILIANI · IMPERATORIS · MVNVS · MCCCCLXXXXIIII · Pearled border.

Hill, *Corpus*, no. 606, pl. 108
Armand, I, 104, I
Herrgott, pl. XVIII, 86
Mazzuchelli, I, pl. XXXI, 2
Litta, *Bentivoglio, Monete*, no. 16
Habich, pl. LXX, I
Friedlaender, p. 173, pl. XXXIV, I
Simon, no. 131
Supino, no. 222
Keary, no. 77
British Museum, *Guide*, p. 22, fig. 24
Hill, *Dreyfus Coll.*, no. 184, pl. XLVI
Migeon, *Les Arts* (August 1908), p. 12, no. XXIII

BOLOGNESE, after FRANCESCO RAIBOLINI called IL FRANCIA c. 1450-c.1517

22

Francesco degli Alidosi, Cardinal Legate of Bologna and Romagna, 1508-11

Bronze medal, 61 mm. diam.

FR · ALIDOXIVS · CAR · PAPIEN · BON · ROMANDIOLAE · Q · C · LEGAT · Bust right, wearing a bishop's cape and beret. Pearled border.

Rev. HIS AVIBVS CVRRVQ CITODVCE RIS ADASTRA. Jupiter, wielding thunderbolt with his left hand, and holding an object of uncertain nature in his right hand, standing on a car drawn to right along clouds by two eagles. Below, signs of Pisces and Sagittarius. Pearled border.

Hill, *Corpus*, no. 610, pl. 109
Armand, II, 116, 45
Bode, *Zeitschrift*, XV (1904), p. 40
Habich, pl. LXX, 5
Tresor, I, pl. XXXIII, 3
Saglio, *L'Art*, LIV (1893), pp. 125-131
Fabriczy, p. 93
Venturi, VI, 800
Foville, p. 55
Revue Numismatique (1914), pp. 98 ff.
Hill, *Medals of the Renaissance*, pp. 64-65
Friedlaender, p. 176, pl. XXXIV
Simon, no. 132
Rizzini, no. 135
Supino, no. 228, pl. XXXI
British Museum, *Select Italian Medals*, pl. 42, 2
British Museum, *Guide*, p. 23, no. 50

Cardinal Francesco degli Alidosi was a favorite of Pope Julius II. After the loss of Bologna to Giangiacomo Trivulzio, the Marshal of France, Alidosi was careless enough to accuse the Pope's nephew, Francesco Maria della Rovere, of misconduct and to blame the military reverses on him. Francesco Maria thereupon stabbed his accuser to death. According to another version of the story, he suspected Alidosi of treachery on behalf of the French.

Provenance: Dr. Benno Geiger Coll.

CRISTOFORO CARADOSSO FOPPA ac. 1475-1527

One of the best artists of the fifteenth century, Foppa is generally known by his second name, Caradosso; he worked chiefly in Milan until the fall of Lodovico il Moro. In 1505 he settled in Rome, where he stayed for the remainder of his life.

His square medal with the portrait of the old warrior, Giangiacomo Trivulzio, is indeed unusual for its shape.

23

Giangiacomo Trivulzio 1441-1518, Marshal of France 1499

Square bronze medal, H. 46 mm., W. 46 mm.

IO IACOBVS TRIVVLS · MAR · VIG · FRA · MARESCALVS · Laureate bust left with long hair, wearing plate armor over gorget of mail. Inscription between two outer and one inner circles; in the four corners are four shields: 1) Trivulzio (paly of six), 2) cross pattée within a flaming circle, 3) biscione on a shield, 4) on a shield, three brands in pale, each carrying two buckets. Double outer border interrupted by these shields.

Rev. Nine lines of inscription: 1499 | EXPVGNATA ALE | XANDRIA: DELETO | EXERCITV : LVDOVI | CVM · SF · MLI DVC | EXPELLIT. REVER | SVM · APVD NOVA | RIAM STERNIT | CAPIT | Below: leaf. Raised linear border.

Hill, *Corpus*, no. 655, pl. 115
Tresor, I, XI, 3
Armand, I, 110, 11
Habich, pl. LXVI, I
Van Mieris, I, p. 328
Koehler, II, p. 49
Litta, *Trivulzio*, no. 1
Detroit Institute of Arts, *Decorative Arts of the Italian Renaissance 1400-1600*, no. 312, ill. p. 139. This specimen.

Commemorates the capture of Alexandria and Trivulzio's appointment as Marshal of France. It is probably one of the best portraits of this great condottiere that have been preserved.

Provenance: Loebbecke Coll., 1908, no. 59, pl. 6

ANDREA GUACIALOTI or GUAZZALOTTI 1435-95

Guacialoti is generally regarded as a member of the Florentine School, although almost all his medals are directly or indirectly connected with Rome. He was a clerk in the Papal Curia until 1467, in which year he retired to a canonry in Prato. There, besides attending to his clerical duties, he cast his own and other artists' medals, one of them the medal by Bertoldo on the Pazzi Conspiracy (see no. 28).

24

Sixtus IV (Francesco della Rovere 1414-84) Pope 1471-84

Bronze medal, 60 mm. diam., 1481

· SIXTVS · IIII · PON · · MAX · SACRICVLT · Bust left, wearing tiara, cope and morse. Pearled border.

Rev. · PARCERE · SVBIECTIS · ET DEBELLARE SVPERBOS; in the exergue: · CONSTANTIA · Across the field: MCCCC-LXXXI (en-

graved) and · SIXTE-POTES Constancy, nude, standing to front, looking left; she rests left arm on fluted column, her right on tall staff, and holds a long scarf passing across her waist. At her feet, on the right, a group of crouching Turkish captives, arms and banners; on left, galleys in the harbor. Pearled border.

The motto is from Virgil (*Aen.* VI, 854). The medal commemorates the expulsion of the Turks from Otranto in 1481 by troops partly contributed by the Pope.

Hill, *Corpus*, no. 751, pl. 126
Armand, I, 50, 10
Bonanni, I, 91, no. 9
Venuti, p. 36, no. VI
Programm zur Jenaischen Literatur-Zeitung (1810), p. VIII
Numismatic Chronicle (1884), p. 182
Heiss, *Florentine Medals*, I, 52, 1; pl. IV, 1
Fabriczy, p. 108, pl. XXI, 2
Martinori, p. 29
Hill, *Roman Medallists*, pp. 30 and 32, pl. I, 5
Habich, pl. XXXIII, 6
Friedlaender, *Andrea Guacialoti*, p. 14, 8; pl. III, 7
Friedlaender, p. 137, 10; pl. XXIV
Rizzini, no. 41
Litta, *Rovere, Sisto IV*, no. 4
Supino, no. 61, pl. XIV
Keary, no. 311
British Museum, *Guide*, p. 24, fig. 26
Louvre, *Catalogue des Bronzes* (Paris 1904), no. 466
Hill, *Dreyfus Coll.*, no. 209, pl. LIII
Migeon, *Les Arts* (August 1908), p. 11, no. X
Forrer, II, 331 (ill.)

LYSIPPUS ac. 1471-84

Known under the pseudonym of "Lysippus the Younger." His real name is unknown. He was the nephew of Cristoforo di Geremia.

Nearly all the artist's clients seem to have been connected with the Papal Curia or Roman University. His medals are distinguished by their fine lettering, their sense of proportion, and the preference for the use of a leaf or pair of leaves as an ornament (see no. 26).

25

Sixtus IV

Bronze medal, 42 mm. diam.

SIXTVS · IIII · PONT · · MAX · SACRI · CVLT · Bust left, wearing tiara, cope, and large circular morse. Pearled border.

Rev. HEC DAMVS IN TERRIS · AETERNA DABVNTVR OLIMPO The Pope, enthroned facing front, wearing cope, hands joined in prayer; a tiara is placed on his head by St. Francis on left (who holds a cross) and St. Anthony on right (who holds a fire); both have the nimbus. Pearled border.

Hill, *Corpus*, no. 807
Armand, II, 62, 1; III, 180, a
Bonanni, p. 91, 3
Venuti, p. 33, III
Tresor, I, XXIV, 3
Numismatic Chronicle (1884), p. 179, I
Thurston, p. 43
Burlington Magazine (1909), p. 280
Martinori, p. 26
Hill, *Roman Medals*, p. 35, pl. V, 3
Habich, pl. LXI, I
Simon, no. 338
Rizzini, no. 39
Litta, *Rovere, Sisto IV*, no. 2
Supino, no. 189

26

Giovanni Alvise Toscani d. 1475, Milanese jurist, orator, and poet.

Bronze medal, 42.5 mm. diam.

IOANNES ALOISIVS · TVSCA · AVDITOR · CAM Bust facing left, wearing round cap and close-fitting gown. Pearled border.

Rev. (two leaves on stalk) VICTA IAM NVRSIA FATIS AGITVR Neptune nude, mantle arched over his head, holding trident in right, dolphin in left, facing front in sea-car drawn by two sea horses. Pearled border.

Hill, *Corpus*, no. 811, pl. 132
Armand, II, 28, 13
Rizzini, no. 443
Mazzuchelli, I, pl. XIX, 4
Supino, no. 155
Tresor, I, pl. XXXIX, 5
Hill, *Dreyfus Coll.*, no. 220, pl. LVI

GIOVANNI CANDIDA (Giovanni di Salvatore Filangieri) c. 1450-c. 1495

Descended from a noble Neapolitan family, Candida grew to distinction in the diplomatic service. In 1477, after the death of Charles the Bold, Candida became secretary to Maximilian I and Mary of Burgundy at the court in Ghent. Maximilian and the beautiful young Mary were married that same year. The charming medal which Candida executed of the pair on the occasion of their marriage is among the artist's notable productions.

The well-known painting by Hans Memling in the Antwerp Gallery of a man holding a coin of Nero may possibly be the portrait of Giovanni Candida, though some experts believe it to represent Niccolo Spinelli.

27

Maximilian of Austria 1459-1519 and *Mary of Burgundy* 1457-82

Bronze medal, 48.4 mm. diam., c. 1477

· MAXIMILIANVS. FR. CAES. F. DVX. AVSTR. BVRGVND Bust right, with long hair confined by twisted fillet and myrtle (?) wreath; open coat over doublet laced across breast. Pearled border.

Rev. MARIA. KAROLI. F. DVX. BVRGVNDIAE. AVSTRIAE. BRAB. C. FLAN: Bust right, hair drawn back and tied in loose knot; plain dress with insertion in front; behind, two M's interlaced and surmounted by crown. Pearled border.

Hill, *Corpus*, no. 831
Armand, II, 80, 1
Habich, pl. LXII, 7

Heraeus, pl. XIV, 7 and pl. XVIII, 7
Van Mieris, I, 141
Herrgott II, pl. I; pl. X, VI
Baldass, XXXI (1925), p. 249
Rizzini, no. 505
British Museum, *Guide*, p. 28, fig. 30

BERTOLDO DI GIOVANNI c. 1420-91

Bertoldo is more often remembered as Donatello's pupil and Michelangelo's master than for his own productions. He did not cast his own medals but, after having made his models, left the casting to others.
The medal on the Pazzi Conspiracy was cast by Andrea Guacialoti. Bertoldo's medals are low relief, usually crowded with many small figures and rather restless.

28

Lorenzo 1449-92 and *Giuliano de Medici* 1453-78

Bronze medal, 63.5 mm. diam.

LAVRENTIVS MEDICES. Bust almost in profile, to the right, placed above the octagonal enclosure of the choir in the Duomo of Florence. Within it, priests are celebrating Mass; outside, conspirators are attacking Lorenzo. Below the bust: SALVS PVBLICA.

Rev. IVLIANVS MEDICES Bust almost in profile, to the left, placed above the choir of the Duomo where Mass is being celebrated. Outside, conspirators killing Giuliano who lies on the ground. Below the bust: LVCTVS PVBLICVS.

Hill, *Corpus*, no. 915, pl. 148
Armand, I, 59, I
Vasari, edizione Milanesi, III, 297
Keary, no. 33
Bode, *Florentiner Bildhauer der Renaissance*, p. 259
Fabriczy, p. 112
Hill, *Medals of the Renaissance*, p. 75
Habich, pl. XXXIV, 4
Bode, *Bertoldo*, p. 26 ff.
Friedlaender, p. 160, 1; pl. XXXI
Rizzini, nos. 84 and 85
Mazzuchelli, I, pl. XXX, 2
Supino, no. 66, pl. XVI
Litta, *Medici*, no. 3
Heiss, *Spinelli*, p. 60 ff., pl. VI, 3
Louvre, *Catalogue des Bronzes* (Paris 1904), no. 469

FLORENTINE, SECOND HALF OF THE FIFTEENTH CENTURY

29

Tito Vespasiano Strozzi 1422-1505, Florentine poet

Rectangular bronze medal, H. 185 mm., W. 132 mm.

Bust with long hair in very high relief facing right, wearing round cap and pleated robe. Below the truncation: TITVS. STROCIVS ·

No reverse.

cf. Hill, *Corpus*, p. 33, no. 125d, 125e

Armand, I, 11, 35 (175 x 111 mm.). Armand judges Strozzi on this medal to be about 50 to 60 years of age, which would date it between 1470-80.

Hill, in his *Corpus*, no. 125, erroneously combines this medal with another from the Ferrarese School (the specimen in Oxford illustrated in *Corpus*), which, however, portrays another person.

Only the piece quoted by Hill as 125d (Paris-Armand, 175 x 111 mm.) and 125e (Turin, no size given) are similar to the present. Another specimen (183 x 128 mm.) was recorded in the Elkan Coll. (Catalogue 1934), no. 70.

The present specimen is the fourth known, and the largest in size.

Provenance: Count Trivulzio Coll.

NICCOLO DI FORZORE SPINELLI called NICCOLO FIORENTINO 1430-1514

His is the most famous name in the history of the Florentine medal. Niccolo's skill is at its best in his splendid portraiture. Powerful style and bold relief, rather than petty details, are the artist's forte.

A painting in the manner of Botticelli, in the Uffizi Gallery, of a young man holding a medal of Cosimo Vecchio, probably represents Niccolo. Some experts have also recognized him in Memling's famous painting at the Antwerp Gallery, showing a man with Florentine long hair, holding a bronze coin of Emperor Nero.

30

Antonio Geraldini 1457-88

Bronze medal, signed, 66.7 mm. diam.

ANTONIVS · GERALDINVS · PONTIFICIVS · LOGOTHETA · FASTORVM · VATES · Bust right with curly hair, wearing round cap and pleated gown.

Rev. · RELIGIO · SANCTA · and, in arc below: the signature · OP · NI · FO · SP · FL · (Opus Nicolai Forzori Spinelli Florentini) Standing figure of Religion facing left, laureate, wears tunic and mantle, swings censer in right hand, holds cornucopia in left hand.

Hill, *Corpus,* no. 924, pl. 150
Armand, I, 84, 2
Bode, *Jahrbuch* xxv, p. 10; pl. B, 8
Habich, pl. xxxvi, 2
Tormo, xxv (1917), p. 61
Friedlaender, p. 140, 3
Heiss, *Spinelli,* p. 13, 3; pl. I, 3

According to Bode, this medal was made in Rome during the stay which he supposes Niccolo to have made there in 1485-86. Geraldini was a colleague of Mendoza, Ambassador of Ferdinand and Isabella, in his embassy in 1486. He was crowned Poet Laureate in 1479. Innocent VIII made him protonotary (logothea). Lancetti, *Memorie Intorno ai Poeti Laureati* (1839), pp. 194 ff.

NICCOLO DI FORZORE SPINELLI called NICCOLO FIORENTINO 1430-1514, attributed to

31

Bernardino Gamberia d. 1507, Bishop of Cavaillon

Bronze medal, 61.2 mm. diam., 1485

· BER · GAMB · INNOCENTII · VIII · C · S · AN · XXX · 1485. Bust left, with thick curly hair, wearing round cap and close-fitting dress.

Rev. SATIABOR CVM APPARVERIT God the Father in clouds.

Hill, *Corpus,* no. 933, pl. 152
Armand, ii, 64, 15
Hill, *Dreyfus Coll.,* no. 260
Bode, *Jahrbuch der Preussischen Kunstsammlungen* xxv (1904), p. 10, pl. B, 10
Simon, no. 175

Gamberia, here "cubicularius secretus," is mentioned frequently by Burckhardt from 1485 onwards.

32

Alamanno Rinuccini 1419-99, Florentine writer and historian

Bronze medal, 87 mm. diam., 1493

ALAMANNVS · RINVCCINVS · PHILIPPI · F Bust left, in very high relief, bareheaded and with long hair, wearing close-fitting dress. Underneath: 1493.

No reverse.

Hill, *Corpus,* no. 1010, pl. 166 (this specimen illustrated)
Armand, iii, 171, D
Cecchi, ill.
Heiss, *Florentine Medals,* i, 145
Burlington Magazine, xxii (1912), 132
Provenance: Baron C. A. de Cosson Coll.

33

Alessandro di Gino Vecchietti 1472-1532

Bronze medal, 77.3 mm. diam., c. 1498

· ALESSANDRO · DI GINO · VECHIETTI · and below bust, · ANNI Z6. Bust right, curly long hair, wearing cap with back flap turned up, and plain robe.

Rev. Nude Fortuna, three-quarters left, advancing over waves on dolphin; holds aloft in right hand halyard of a sail, sheet of which she holds in her left hand; in front of her, on the waves, radiant sun's face. On right, on a rock, an ermine, holding in its mouth a scroll inscribed PRIVS · MORI · QVAM TVRPARI ·

The arms of the Vecchietti of Florence are five ermines rampant, silver on blue.

Hill, *Corpus,* no. 1027, pl. 170
Armand, i, 99, 4
Habich, pl. xlvi, 1
Bode, *Jahrbuch der Preussischen Kunstsammlungen* xxv, 8, pl. B, 4
Heiss, *Florentine Medals,* i, p. 89; pl. xiii, 6
Friedlaender, p. 154, 35; pl. xxx
Supino, no. 118
Archivo Storico dell'Arte iii (1890), p. 30
Calvo y del Rivero, pl. xvi, 3 (Museo Arqueologico Nacional)
Provenance: Count Trivulzio Coll.

Girolamo Savonarola 1452-98

Bronze medal, 93 mm. diam.

· HIERONX[!]MVS · SAVᵒ · FER · VIR · DOCTISSˢ · ORDINIS · PREDICHATORVM   Bust left in habit with hood raised.

Rev. · GLADIVS · DOMINI SVP · TERAM · CITOET VELOCITER
Divine hand holding dagger, threatening the cities of Venice, Milan, Genoa, Florence, Pisa, Rome, Naples, and another city, probably Bologna.

Hill, *Corpus,* no. 1075, pl. 179
Armand, II, 46, 17
Heiss, *Spinelli,* p. 69, 3; pl. VII, 1
Migeon, *Les Arts,* August 1908, p. 8, v
Hill, *Dreyfus Coll.,* no. 282
Hofstede de Groot, 17, 6, 1929, no. 31 (92 mm.)

Portrait of most powerful expression. The only medallic Savonarola portrait of great merit.

According to Hill, the design of this medal is doubtless due to one of the sons of Andrea della Robbia. The reverse legend records predictions by Savonarola of the fate of Florence; the sword of the Lord is the French invasion, which he predicted.

FLORENTINE, LATE FIFTEENTH-EARLY SIXTEENTH CENTURIES

35

Dante Alighieri 1265-1321

Bronze medal, 52 mm. diam.

· DANTHES · FLOREN TINVS   Bust left, wearing laureate cap with falling point and stringed flaps covering ears; gown with small lapels.

Rev. No inscription. Dante before the Mountain of Purgatory. Wearing cap as on obverse, and long robe, he stands at the left, holding book in his left hand, raising his right, and gazing at the mountain on summit of which is the Earthly Paradise, with Adam and Eve under the Tree of Knowledge; in a cavity at base of mountain, two figures; halfway up, an arch; to the left, a lesser mountain with two entrances to Hell with demons, etc., about them; above, seven circles of Heaven.

Hill, *Corpus,* 1092
Armand, II, 11, 1
Habich, pl. XLIX, 1
Heiss, *Florentine Medals,* I, 125, 1; pl. XVII, 1
Holbrook, title page and pp. 240-241
Friedlaender, p. 154, no. 37; pl. XXX
Passerini, p. 43
Tresor, I, XIV, 3
Numismatic Chronicle (1913), p. 414, pl. XX, 1

The reverse of this medal is based on the painting made in 1465 by Domenico di Michelino in the Duomo, Florence. Cf. the early Florentine engraving (Hind, A, I, 23).

BENVENUTO CELLINI, SCHOOL OF, SIXTEENTH CENTURY

36

Unknown Nobleman, possibly Cosimo de' Medici, 1519-74; married 1539 to Eleonora de Toledo; Duke of Florence 1537-69, Grand Duke of Tuscany 1569-74

Octagonal buff-colored honestone bijou, H. 56 mm., W. 42 mm.

Bareheaded bust with short beard to left, wearing armor with lions' heads on both shoulders, over shirt with turned-down collar.

Rev. Painted with interlacing scrolls and leaf patterns centered by a fleur-de-lis, in tones of brown, white, and gold.

The stone panel is set in a contemporary octagonal gold frame with open-work border, enamelled in red, white, green, and blue. Original suspension loop. Outside dimension of frame: H. 87 mm., W. 63 mm.

Otrange-Mastai, p. 127, no. 11 (this specimen)

The style of this piece, as well as the workmanship of the enamelled frame, would point toward an attribution to Benvenuto Cellini. The artist worked from 1545 to 1571 in Florence, and it is known that he cut in hard materials like honestone, slate, and crystal. Another Italian honestone model, depicting Alessandro Piccolomini, is in the Munich State Coll. (M. Bernhart, *Nachtraege zu Armand,* Archiv v, p. 82).

Unique

Provenance: Martin J. Desmoni Coll., Sotheby, May 17, 1960, no. 96, pl. 18

ITALIAN MEDALS FROM THE TIME OF BENVENUTO CELLINI ONWARDS

FLORENTINE ARTISTS

PASTORINO DE' PASTORINI Siena 1508-1592 Florence

Although a native son of Siena (his father was a shoemaker at, or from the neighborhood of, Siena), Pastorino worked in the Florentine tradition. His early years were spent on glass painting, but from 1540 to 1578 he devoted himself to the modelling of portraits in wax and casting them, usually in lead and without reverse. His casts are so finely executed that at first glance they almost appear to be struck.

Judging by the number of medals by Pastorino, it would appear that he was not only one of the most prolific artists of the sixteenth century, but a popular one as well. Vasari says of him, "he copied all the world, and persons of all kinds. ..." He portrayed with great skill many ladies of the Italian Renaissance. His highly developed feeling for grace and minute detail in the presentation of their likenesses is evident (see no. 38).

37

Lodovico Ariosto 1474-1533

Bronze medal, 38 mm. diam.

LVDOVICVS ARIOST POET Laureate and bearded head of the poet facing left. Pearled border.

Rev. PRO BONO MALVM Bees surrounding a column rising from amidst flames. Pearled border.

Armand, I, 188, 2
Tresor, II, XXXVI, 4
Van Mieris, II, 377
Koehler, XVII, 33
Loebbecke Coll., Munich 1908, no. 53
Habich, pl. LXXXIV, 6
Forrer, IV, 409 (ill.)
Mazzuchelli, I, LXVII, 4

38

Lucrezia de' Medici 1545-61, first wife of Alfonso II

Lead medal, 69 mm. diam., 1558

LVCRETIA · MED · FERR · PRINC · A · A · XIII · Bust left, hair wound back and ornamented with string of jewels, wearing richly embroidered robe, earring and necklace with pendant. Above truncation, artist's signature: P. Below truncation: 1558.

No reverse.

Armand, I, 195, 40

Made probably on the occasion of Lucrezia's marriage to Alfonso II d'Este in 1558.

GIANPAOLO POGGINI Florence 1518-c. 1582 Madrid

Poggini was born into a family of artists. His father Michele was a gem-engraver, his younger brother Domenico, like himself, a medallist of renown. He is best known for his fine medals of Philip II and his family.

39

Philip II 1527-98, King of Spain 1556-98

Silver medal, 42 mm. diam., 1559

· PHILIPPVS HISPANIAR · ET NOVI ORBIS OCCIDVI REX Bareheaded bust with short beard facing left, wearing cuirass. Below truncation, artist's signature: I · PAVL · POG · F · Pearled border.

Rev. PACE. TERRA. MARIQ. COMPOSITA Standing Pax, holding horn of plenty, sets fire to a pile of armaments in front of the closed Temple of Janus. In the exergue: · MDLIX · Pearled border.

Armand, I, 238, 5
Van Loon, I, 28
Cicognara, II, LXXXV, 2
Habich, pl. LXXX, 5, 6
Vidal Quadras y Ramon, no. 13609
Le Maistre, no. 13
Betts, no. 3
Forrer, IV, 633

Commemorates the peace treaty of Chateau Cambresis. The remarkable obverse legend cites Philip as King of Spain and of the New World in the West.

DOMENICO POGGINI Florence 1520-1590 Rome

A goldsmith, sculptor, die-engraver, and medallist, Poggini began his artistic career together with his brother Gianpaolo. A prolific artist, his medallic creations alone comprise about fifty pieces.

40

Cosimo I de' Medici 1519-74, Duke of Florence 1537-69, Grand Duke of Tuscany 1569-74

Silver medal, 41.5 mm. diam., 1567

COSMVS MED · FLOREN · ET SENAR · DVX · II · Bareheaded bust right with short beard, wearing cuirass and drapery. On the breast: 1567. Pearled border.

Rev. QVO · MELIOR · OPTABILIOR · In a hexagonal basin, fed by aqueduct, stands Neptune, brandishing his trident, on a chariot drawn by two sea horses. Pearled border.

Armand, I, 261, 41
Litta, *Medici,* no. 31
cf. Forrer, IV, 629

PIETRO PAOLO GALEOTTI generally known as PIETRO PAOLO ROMANO called IL ROMANO d. 1584

A goldsmith, coin engraver, and medallist, Il Romano, a native of Rome, worked in the north of Italy, settled at Florence in 1550, and died there in 1584.

Il Romano's medals are executed with much care and in a manner at once graceful and expressive.

41

Faustina Sforza Marchesa of Caravaggio, married 1546

Bronze medal, 72 mm. diam.

FAVSTINA SFORTIA MARCH CARAVAGII. Bust facing right, veiled and richly draped, wearing double necklace. In the field, to the right, a vine leaf.

No reverse.

cf. Armand, I, 234, 35

42

Gianfrancesco Trivulzio d. 1573, Marchese of Vigevano and Castelnuovo

Bronze medal, 59.5 mm. diam.

The grandson of Giangiacomo Trivulzio, he lost his possession in the battle of Pavia, but in 1535 was restored by Charles V.

(rosette) IO · FRAN · TRI · MAR · VIG · CO · MVSO · AC · VAL · REN · ET · STOSA · D · Bearded and cuirassed bust right, drapery fastened on right shoulder. On the truncation: AET · 39 ·

Rev. FVI SVM ET ERO. Nude Fortuna, holding flowing sail amidst a violent sea, surrounded by dolphins and tritons. Above and below, four blowing zephyrs.

Armand, II, 302, 13
Forrer, II, 192
Habich, pl. XCVI, 5
Provenance: Dr. Jacob Hirsch Estate

GASPARE MOLA c. 1580-c. 1640

As a youth Mola was apprenticed to a Milan goldsmith. The bronze gates of the Cathedral of Pisa, about 1601, were his first major commission. During his early period of activity he worked at Florence, and from 1613-14 at the mints of Guastalla and Mantua. In 1623 the artist settled in Rome, and was appointed Papal mint engraver in 1625, succeeding Jacobo Antonio Moro. Habich writes about Mola: "His best works show the influence of the brilliant French medallist Guillaume Dupré, with whom Mola had contact." Mola was a master at depicting even the most minute detail.

43

Charles Emanuel I 1562-1630, Duke of Savoy 1580-1630

Oval gold medal, H. 58 mm., W. 45.5 mm., 1606

CAROLVS · EMAN · D · G · DVX · SAB · P · P · Bareheaded bust with beard and moustache to right, wearing ruff collar, richly damascened armor and drapery; around the neck an embroidered ribbon from which a medallion is suspended. The ribbon doubly inscribed: FERT (the motto

of the House of Savoy, whose meaning has been explained as: Foedere Et Religione Tenemur). Under the truncation, the artist's signature: GASP · M ·

Rev. OPORTVNE The centaur Chiron, bearded and with flying stole, prancing right, shooting his arrow. On his body the constellation Sagittarius ("The Archer"); beneath his hooves the planetary system. Below, the date MDCVI. Original suspension loop.

Forrer IV, 113 (ill.)

The centaur Chiron, son of Titan Chronos, ancestor of Achilles and Ajax, was the famous teacher of Jason, Asklepios, and Herakles. When he received an incurable wound he gave his immortality to Prometheus. Chiron became the constellation Sagittarius.

This gold medal is the earliest and probably the finest by Mola.

44

Cosimo II de' Medici 1590-1620, Grand Duke of Tuscany 1608-20

Silver oval medal, H. 48 mm., W. 40 mm.

Youthful bust right, with short hair and small moustache, wearing armor with Maltese cross on breastplate.

No reverse.

Unpublished and probably unique.

cf. Fabriczy, p. 183, pl. XXXVI, 5
cf. Habich, p. 119, pl. LXXXII, 8

ANTONIO SELVI d. 1755

Selvi was one of the most prolific Florentine artists, and a pupil of Massimiliano Soldani-Benzi. He is said to have resided in England for a while.

45

Cosimo I de' Medici 1519-74, Duke of Florence 1537-69, Grand Duke of Tuscany 1569-74

Bronze medal, 85 mm. diam.

MAGNVS · COSMVS · MEDICES · P · P · P · Bust right, wearing gown and round cap. Raised border.

Rev. SEMPER Three interlinked rings. Raised border.

Hill, *Corpus,* no. 1110, 9
Armand, II, 25, 1
Mazzuchelli, I, pl. XX, 3

ROMAN ARTISTS

ALESSANDRO CESATI called IL GRECO or IL GRECHETTO ac. 1538-53

Cesati was born on Cyprus about 1500, the son of an Italian father and a Cypriote mother. He is mentioned by Vasari as the first medallist of his age. "Far beyond others," Vasari says, "has gone Alessandro Cesati, called Il Greco, by whom every other artist is surpassed in the grace and perfection as well as in the universality of his productions."

46

Dido, Queen of Carthage

Bronze medal, 45 mm. diam.

Greek inscription: DIDO BASILISSA. Bust right, wreathed, hair in coils and falling on neck, drapery fastened on right shoulder. Pearled border.

Rev. Greek inscription: KARCHEDON View of Carthage, with galleys lying in harbor before it.

Hill, *Dreyfus Coll.,* no. 368, pl. LXXXVI
cf. *Burlington Magazine,* February 1911, p. 267, pl. II, 8

GIAN FEDERIGO BONZAGNA called FEDERIGO PARMENSE ac. 1547-75

An artist of stature of the second half of the sixteenth century, medallic products by Bonzagna are not known after 1575, though he was still alive in 1586. He worked at the Papal mint in Rome and also for Pierluigi and Ottavio Farnese in Parma.

Two especially fine plaquettes by Parmense will be found as nos. 165 and 166.

Pierluigi Farnese 1503-47, Duke of Parma and Piacenza

Bronze medal, 39 mm. diam.

· P(etrus) · LOYSIVS · F(arnesius) · PARM(ae) · ET · PLAC(entiae) · DVX · I · Bearded, bareheaded bust right, wearing mantle, shirt of mail, and damascened cuirass with lion's head on right shoulder. Under truncation, the artist's signature: F · PARM · Legend between pearled circles.

Rev. · AD · CIVITAT(is) · DITIONISQ(ue) TVTEL(am) MVNIM-(entum) · EXTRVCTVM · Bird's-eye view of the citadel of Parma, with gate opening on a stream. Legend between pearled circles.

Armand, I, 222, 6
Litta, *Farnese,* II, I
Hill, *Dreyfus Coll.,* no. 375, pl. LXXXVII
Forrer, I, 214
Provenance: Loebbecke Coll., Munich 1908, no. 87
             Gutekunst Coll., Stuttgart 1910, no. 60, pl. IV

Pius V (Michele Ghislieri 1504-72) Pope 1566-72

Gilded bronze medal, 37.5 mm. diam., 1571

PIVS · V · PONT(ifex) · OPT(imus) · MAX(imus) · ANNO · VI · Bearded bust left, wearing skullcap and cape with hood. Below, the artist's signature: F(edericus) P(armensis). Pearled border.

Rev. DEXTERA TVA · DOM(ine) · PERCVSSIT · INIMICVM · 1571 · View of the Battle of Lepanto; on a galley, an angel with cross and chalice; God hurling lightning from above. Pearled border.

Armand, I, 226, 33
Tresor, Medailles Papales, pl. XV, 4
Bolzenthal, I, 291, 11
Hill, *Dreyfus Coll.,* no. 373, pl. LXXXVII
Vogel Coll., no. 43

The reverse legend on this medal is taken from *Exodus,* 15, 6.

The medal commemorates the victorious Battle of Lepanto.

Pius V is the last Pope to have been canonized.

GASPARO MORONE-MOLA ac. 1627-c. 1668

A nephew of Gaspare Mola (cf. nos. 43 ff.), he entered into partnership with his uncle and Orazio Ghibellini for the production of medals. Upon his uncle's death, he was appointed engraver at the Papal mint in Rome. The following piece belongs to the period of his earliest works.

Vincenzo II Gonzaga Duke of Mantua 1626-27

Silver medal, 46 mm. diam.

VINCEN · II · D · G · DVX · MANT · VII · ET · M · F · V · (Vincentius secundus, Dei gratia, dux Mantuae VII et Montisferratis V) Bareheaded bust with long hair and moustache facing left, wearing ruff collar and adorned cuirass, neck chain with jewel. Under the truncation, the artist's signature: G · MORON · F(ecit) · Pearled border.

Rev. FERIS · TANTVM · INFENSVS · A hound standing to left. Pearled border.

Corpus, p. 359, 25
Forrer, IV, 156

GIOACHINO FRANCESCO TRAVANI mid-seventeenth century

In 1655, Travani was one of the three "Consuls" of the goldsmiths' guild in Rome. Among his best-known productions is the medal of Queen Christina of Sweden, who after her abdication and conversion to the Catholic Church had retired to Rome. Christina is represented as the "Pallas Nordica."

Christina 1626-89, Queen of Sweden 1632-54

Silver medal, 61 mm. diam., 1665

· REGINA · · CHRISTINA · Head as Pallas Athena facing right. Granulated field.

Rev. (in Greek letters) MAKELOS (Swedish: without peer). Phoenix rising from the ashes. In the exergue: 1665. Granulated field.

Hildebrand, I, no. 104a
Crona Coll., no. 260 (bronze)
Forrer, VI, 129 (ill.)
De Bildt, pl. VI, nos. 26 and 27

GIOVANNI HAMERANI 1649-1705

Giovanni Hamerani, who in 1677 succeeded his father Alberto as Papal medallist, was perhaps the most distinguished of the Hamerani family of die-cutters.

Innocent XII (Antonio Pignatelli 1615-1700) Pope 1691-1700

Gold medal, 32 mm. diam., 1691

INNOCEN · XII · PONT · M · A · I · (anno I). Bust right, with short beard, wearing camauro and embroidered cope. Under the truncation, the artist's signature: HAMERA. Pearled border.

Rev. A · DEO · ET · PRO · DEO · Caritas standing, facing front, holding in her arms a child, and flanked by two others who are bearing urns from which flow streams of coins. At her feet, an urn spilling coins. Pearled border.

Forrer, II, 402

Innocent XII was elected Pope as a result of a compromise, but soon showed himself a stern reformer, especially regarding nepotism, which he abolished.

PADUAN ARTISTS

VALERIO BELLI 1468-1546

A native of Vicenza, Belli ranks, however, as a Paduan artist. Chiefly an engraver of crystal and gems, he also cut dies for coins and medals.

Emperor Aelius A.D. 138, adopted son of Emperor Hadrian

Bronze medal, 36 mm. diam.

L(ucius) AELIVS CAESAR Draped bust, bearded and with curly hair, facing right.

Rev. Aelius seated on a podium, before him five armed soldiers with captive. In the exergue: S. C.

From the series of the "Twelve Caesars" by Valerio Belli.

Forrer, I, 158

GIOVANNI DAL CAVINO called IL PADOVANO 1500-70

Cavino is well known for his imitations of Roman large bronze coins and medallions, numbering about 120. The portraits mostly belong to the period of the "Twelve Caesars," though he does not neglect some of their successors. His work is typical of the spirit of the Renaissance, bringing back to life the heritage of classical antiquity.

Floriano Antonini

Bronze medal, 38 mm. diam.

FLORIANVS ANTONINVS ANDREAE · F · Bearded bust with short hair right, wearing buttoned coat.

Rev. Below exergue line: AETERNITATI SACRVM Various persons in front of a two-story building, the frieze of which is adorned with a bas-relief.

Mazzuchelli, I, LXIV, 5
Armand, I, 179, 2

Agrippina Sr. d. A.D. 33, daughter of Marcus Agrippa, wife of Germanicus

Bronze medal, 36.5 mm. diam.

AGRIPPINA M(arci) F(ilia) · MAT(er) · C(aii) · CAESARIS. AVGVSTI Bust right, hair in club behind, tresses falling down neck, drapery over shoulder.

Rev. S · P · Q · R | MEMORIAE | AGRIPPINAE Funeral car drawn by two mules.

Forrer, I, 367 (ill.)
Hill, *Dreyfus Coll.*, pl. XCI, 401 (variant)
Cohen, I, 231, I
Lawrence, no. 7

55

Emperor Otho A.D. 69

Bronze medal, 36 mm. diam.

· IMP(erator) · OTHO · CAESAR · AVG(ustus) · TRI(bunicia) · POT(estatis). Bust right, wearing undulated hairpiece.

Rev. SECVRITAS · P(opuli) · R(omani) · Otho before an altar extending his hand to four armed soldiers carrying military standards before an altar. In the exergue: S C.

Cohen, I, 354 (note)
Forrer, I, 368
Lawrence, no. 23

The types of this medal were invented by Cavino. The Romans did not issue Sestertii of Otho.

56

Emperor Vitellius A.D. 69

Bronze medal, 35 mm. diam.

A(ulus) VITELLIVS GERMAN(icus) IMP(erator) AVG(ustus) P(ontifex) M(aximus) TR(ibunus) Draped and laureate bust right.

Rev. Helmeted Mars, his mantle flowing, striding toward the right, carrying a transversal sceptre and a shouldered trophy of armaments. In the field, S - C.

Cohen, I, 362, 80 (variant)
Forrer, I, 368
Lawrence, no. 28

57

Emperor Titus A.D. 79-81

Bronze medal, 34 mm. diam.

IMP(erator) T(itus) CAES(ar) VESP(asianus) AVG(ustus) P(ontifex) M(aximus) TR(ibunicia) P(otestatis) P(ater) P(atriae) COS(ul) VIII Laureate head left.

Rev. IVDAEA CAPTA Under a palm tree, a captive Judaean standing beside captured armaments, and the seated Judaea in attitude of mourning. In the exergue: S C.

Cohen, I, 439, 114
Forrer, I, 368
Lawrence, no. 37

58

Emperor Nerva A.D. 96-98

Bronze medal, 35 mm. diam.

IMP(erator) NERVA CAES(ar) AVG(ustus) P(ontifex) M(aximus) TR(ibunicia) P(otestatis) COS(ul) II P(ater) P(atriae) Laureate bust right.

Rev. CONGIAR P R The emperor holding scroll seated facing right, on curule chair placed on a suggestum, presiding at a congiarium; before him, a prefect distributing gifts to a citizen who is mounting the steps of the suggestum; behind, soldiers and Liberalitas. In the exergue: S C.

Cohen, II, 4, 37
Forrer, I, 368
Lawrence, no. 44

59

Marciana, d. A.D. 114, sister of Emperor Trajan

Medallion, silver core within a bronze rim, 39.5 mm. diam.

DIVA AVGVSTA MARCIANA Draped bust right, wearing triple diadem on elaborately arranged hair.

Rev. CONSECRATIO Marciana, as Vesta, seated on a car drawn by four elephants. In the exergue: S(enatus) P(opulus) Q(ue) R(omae).

60

Emperor Marcus Aurelius A.D. 161-180

Bronze medal, 37 mm. diam.

M. ANTONINVS AVG(ustus) TR(ibunicia) P(otestatis) XXIX Bearded and laureate bust right, wearing drapery over cuirass adorned with aegis on breast.

Rev. IMP(erator) VII COS(ul) III Winged Victory seated to right on armaments, holding a palm branch and a shield inscribed VIC(toria) AVG(usti); in front of her, a military trophy.

Forrer, I, 369
Lawrence, no. 56

61

Faustina Jr. d. A.D. 176, wife of Marcus Aurelius

Bronze medallion, 34 mm. diam.

FAVSTINA AVG(usta) ANTONINI AVG(usti) PII FIL(ia). Draped bust right, hair confined by fillet and in chignon.

Rev. Sacrifice by the Empress and five women and a child before a hexagonal temple containing a statue of Vesta (?). Below: S C.

Cohen, III, 101
Hill, *Dreyfus Coll.*, pl. XCII, 407
Forrer, I, 369
Lawrence, no. 59

62

Emperor Lucius Verus A.D. 161-169

Bronze medallion, 38 mm. diam.

L(ucius) VERVS AVG(ustus) ARM(eniacus) · PARTH(icus) MAX(imus) TR(ibunicia) P(otestatis) VIIII Laureate and bearded bust right, wearing drapery over cuirass.

Rev. Jupiter seated right upon the seven hills of Rome, receiving the Emperor who holds Victory and is crowned by Virtus. In the exergue: TR(ibunicia) P(otestatis) VII. IMP(erator) · IIII · · COS(ul) III · P(ater) · P(atriae) ·

Cohen, III, 197
Forrer, I, 369
Lawrence, no. 60

VENETIAN ARTISTS

ANDREA SPINELLI d. 1572

Spinelli, a native of Parma, was a medallist and mint engraver at Venice during the middle of the sixteenth century. He started his career in 1535 as assistant engraver at the Venice mint, and was appointed chief engraver in 1540. In 1543 he ventured into business, together with his son Giacomo, and dealt in books and engravings.

63

Andrea Gritti Doge 1523-39

Bronze medal, 37 mm. diam., 1534

· ANDREAS · GRITI · DVX · VENETIAR · MDXXXIIII · Bearded bust left, wearing ducal hat and robe. Legend between two pearled borders.

Rev. (leaf) DIVI · FRANCISCI · MDXXXIIII (leaf) View of the church of San Francesco della Vigna at Venice. Below exergue line, the artist's signature: AN · SP · F · Legend between two pearled borders.

Armand, I, 155, 4
Tresor, I, XXVIII, 2
Habich, pl. LXXVI, 16
Hill, *Dreyfus Coll.*, no. 413, pl. XCIII

VITTORIA DELLA VOLPE called ALESSANDRO VITTORIA
Trieste 1525-1608 Venice

Next to Sansovino's, Vittoria's name figures prominently among the Venetian artists of the sixteenth century. Forrer, in his *Dictionary of Medallists*, writes: "In 1562, the year when one of the Rangoni medals was produced, Vittoria was received into the Confraternity of San Marco, when (according to the inscription on the following medal) Rangoni presided over the Brotherhood as a Guardian."

64

Tommaso Rangoni d. 1577, physician and professor in Padua

Bronze medal, 40 mm. diam., 1562

THOM · PHILOL · RAVEN · PHYS · EQ · GVARD · D · MAR · MAG
Bareheaded and bearded bust right, wearing tight-fitting gown. In the field, to the left, 1562.

Rev. · A · IOVE · ET · SORORE · GENITA · An eagle places a child on the breast of a reclining woman (the birth of Hebe).

Armand, II, 196, 19
Forrer, VI, 289 (ill.)
Loebbecke Coll., Munich 1908, no. 42
Lanna Coll., III, no. 164, pl. 12

MILANESE ARTISTS

LEONE LEONI called ARETINUS 1509-90

A sculptor, goldsmith, medallist, and die-engraver, Leoni probably was the most important artist of the Milanese School during the sixteenth century. His violent temper caused him to be committed to the galleys in 1540, and it was to the Genoese Admiral Andrea Doria that he owed his liberation. Even with old age the artist did not mellow, and on one occasion he nearly murdered the son of Titian, trying to rob him, when the latter had come to Milan to collect a large sum of money.

As an artist, Leoni deserves great praise. His medals, retaining many of the sculptural qualities of his predecessors of the fifteenth century, are certainly the work of an artist of broad scope. Charles V was very fond of Leoni's work and, in recognition thereof, ennobled him in 1549, during the artist's sojourn at Brussels.

65

Daniel de Hanna (a member of the well-known Flemish merchant family that settled in Venice)

Bronze medal, 54 mm. diam.

DANIEL (rose) DE (rose) HANNA Bust left, with short hair and beard, wearing cloak fastened with bulla on left shoulder, over figured underdress. Pearled border.

Rev. OMNE VANVM Female figure (Vanity), wearing tunic girt high and mantle, standing to front, looking left, holding in both hands a vase from which smoke emerges. Pearled border.

Armand, I, 169, 29; III, 72, ee
Cicognara, IV, 198
Venice, Correr: Bergman, II, 4, no. 11
Hauschild, *Anhang,* no. 363
T. Whitcombe Greene, no. 93
British Museum
Copenhagen
The present piece is the largest of the recorded specimens.

66

Ippolita Gonzaga 1535-63, wife of Antonio Caraffa

Bronze medal, 68.6 mm. diam.

HIPPOLYTA · GONZAGA · FERDINANDI · FIL · AN · XVI, and in the right field (in Greek) LEON ARETINOS. Bust left, with hair wound into a chignon, wearing dress draped in the antique manner, double pearl necklace with pendant. Pearled border.

Rev. PAR · VBIQ · POTESTAS · Diana blowing her horn marching right, holding an arrow, and accompanied by three hunting dogs. Pluto, with Cerberus at his feet, is seated in a building to the left.

Armand, I, 163, 7
Habich, pl. XCII, 6
Plon, pl. XXXII, 7 and 8
Provenance: Elkan Coll., no. 78

67

Gianello della Torre d. 1583

Bronze medal, 80.8 mm. diam.

Born in Cremona, Della Torre was an engineer and achitect in the service of Charles V. He constructed a hydraulic machine to raise the level of the Tagus River, to which the reverse of this medal may refer. The obverse legend refers to a clock he made for Charles V, who had asked him to repair the one by Giovanni Dondi at Pavia.

IANELLVS · TVRRIAN · CREMON · HOROLOG · ARCHITECT
Bust right, with short hair and beard, wearing tunic and cloak. Pearled border.

Rev. VIR TVS and, in the exergue: NVNQ:DEFICIT A female figure (Fountain of the Sciences) standing, draped, holding on her head a vessel from which escape two jets of water, which various persons in different attitudes collect in vases below. Pearled border.

Armand, I, 170, 38
Plon, pl. XXXIV, nos. 8 and 9, p. 274
Habich, pl. XCIII, 8 (as Jacopo da Trezzo)
Mazzuchelli, I, pl. XLIX, I
Herrera, 9 (1905), pp. 226-270
Fabriczy, pl. XXXIX, 4
Hill, *Dreyfus Coll.,* no. 435, pl. XCVI
Lanna Coll., no. 227, pl. 15
Loebbecke Coll., Munich 1908, no. 121, pl. VIII
There also exists a painted portrait of Gianello by Titian (see: Jean Babelon, *Revue de l'Antiquité Ancienne,* 1913, October, pp. 269-278).

JACOPO NIZZOLA DA TREZZO called JACOPO DA TREZZO
Milan 1515/20-1589 Madrid

Trezzo, a contemporary of Leone Leoni's and like him a distinguished Milanese medallist, entered into the employ of the Emperor, as was customary for leading artists in that period. From 1555 to 1559 he was active in The Netherlands, where his name appears in the state records. In 1559 he left for Spain and stayed there for the remainder of his life, working for the Spanish monarchs in the many artistic crafts that marked his versatility.

68

Ippolita Gonzaga 1535-63, wife of Antonio Caraffa

Bronze medal, 68.5 mm. diam., 1552

HIPPOLYTA · GONZAGA · FERDINANDI · FIL · AN · XVII Bust facing left, with upbound hair, wearing richly draped robe, earring, two necklaces (one with pendant). Below truncation: IAC TREZ. Pearled border.

Rev. VIRTVTIS FORMAEQ PRAEVIA Aurora riding through the heavens in a chariot drawn by Pegasus; holding a torch in her left hand, and with her right strewing flowers over the earth. Pearled border.

Armand, I, 241, I
Hill, *Dreyfus Coll.,* no. 438, pl. XCVI
Rodocanachi, p. 220
Provenance: Luccardi Coll., no. 11, pl. 41

UNIDENTIFIED ARTISTS

NORTH ITALIAN, SIXTEENTH CENTURY

69

Giovanni di Nale b. 1511

Bronze medal, 65 mm. diam., 1544

GIOVANNI DI NALE · Bearded bust with short curly hair facing left, wearing plain robe with lace trim on round collar, loose drapery over shoulders.

Rev. Circle of inscription: D'ETA DI XXXIII ANNI · M · D · XLIIII ·

Armand, III, 235, E (this specimen)

This is the only known specimen.

VENETIAN, SIXTEENTH CENTURY

70

Trifone Gabrielli d. 1549, Venetian patrician and poet

Bronze medal, 44.5 mm. diam.

· TRYPHON GABRIEL · Bareheaded bust left, wearing patrician robe.

Rev. INNOCENS MANIB ET MVNDO CORDE Draped female figure (Innocence) washing her hands at a spring gushing from a high rock.

Armand, II, 126, 10

71

Marcantonio Trevisan Doge 1553-54

Bronze medal, 63.5 mm. diam., 1554

· MARCVS · ANT · TREVISANO · DVX · V · Bearded bust right, wearing ermined robe and ducal cap.

Rev. Within an olive wreath: · MARCVS · | · ANTONIVS · | · TRE-VIXANO · | DEI GRATIA DVX | VENETIARVM | ETC VIXITA-NO · I | IN PRINCIPATV | OBIT · MDLIIII

Hill, *Dreyfus Coll.*, no. 504, pl. CVIII

cf. Armand, II, 224, 1

72

Girolamo Priuli Doge 1559-67

Bronze medal, 42 mm. diam., 1567

HIERONIMVS · PRIOL · VE · DVX : Bearded bust right, wearing brocaded gown and ducal hat.

Rev. I · PV · AN · | VIII · ME · II · DI · | IIII OBI · A · M · | DLXVII · M · | N · D^E · IIII ·

Armand, II, 225, 4

Tresor, II, XXVII, 5

73

Cornelio Musso d. 1574, Bishop of Bitunto

Bronze medal, 58 mm. diam.

CORNELIVS · MVSSVS · EP · BITVNT · His bearded bust right, wearing habit with lowered hood.

Rev. DIVINVM CONCINIT ORBI · Swan left, with spread wings.

Armand, II, 212, 48

cf. Habich, pl. XCV, 4

cf. *Lanna Coll.*, III, no. 312

Forrer, II, 192 (as Pietro Paolo Galeoti, Il Romano)

Francesco Cornelio Musso was called "the Isocrates of Italy."

74

Marino Grimani Doge 1595-1606

Bronze medal, 39 mm. diam., 1595

MARIN. GRIMANVS DVX · VENETIAR Bearded bust right, wearing brocaded robe and ducal hat.

Rev. · SYDERA · · CORDIS · and below exerguel line: · 1595 The haloed lion of St. Mark, rampant to left, holding crosslet orb.

Armand, II, 273, 1

Tresor, II, XXVII, 3

Vogel Coll., no. 56

MILANESE, SIXTEENTH CENTURY

75

Pietro Piantanida Milanese Captain

Bronze medal, 50.5 mm. diam.

CAP · PET · PLANTANIDA · AET · AN · XXXVI Bareheaded bust right, with short hair and beard, wearing drapery over damascened breast armor, adorned with aegis and griffin's head on right shoulder.

Rev. DVM · SPIRITVS · HOS · REGET · ARTVS Draped female figure, standing towards the left, raising her right arm and holding a cup in her left hand (Faith?).

Armand, II, 179, 9 (49 mm.), after Cabinet de France
Burlington Magazine, October 1910, pl. II, B (attributed to Benvenuto Cellini)
Habich, pl. LXXXIII, 4, p. 121
Regling, p. 93
Hill, *Dreyfus Coll.,* no. 423, pl. XCIV
Simonis, II, pl. XXIII, 5 (attributed to Etienne de Hollande)
Habich, *Corpus,* II, 2, p. 487, fig. 507a (as early Italian work of Antonio Abondio)

The present piece is the largest of the recorded specimens.

76

Francesco Panigarola Bishop of Asti 1548-94

Bronze medal, 61 mm. diam., c. 1576

FRANCESCO · PANIGAROLA · AETA · ANNI · XXVIII between three linear circles. Pearled border. Bareheaded bust with curly hair and short beard facing left, wearing buttoned gown with ruffled collar.

No reverse.

Armand, II, 262, 3
Mazerole, I, XCVI, 2
Provenance: Luccardi Coll., pl. 40, no. 5, this specimen

77

Battista Spinola de Serravalis b. 1537, Genoese nobleman

Bronze medal, 47.5 mm. diam.

BAP SPINOLA D · SERRAVALLIS Bareheaded and bearded bust left, wearing ruff collar and cuirass adorned with standing female figure and, on shoulder, lion's head. Around, granitura.

Rev. Hebrew inscription: "Oh Lord, help us." A two-masted ship on a raging sea, two zephyrs blowing from above. Pearled border.

Armand, II, 209, 30 (example seen in Heiss Coll.)

FRENCH MEDALS

NICOLAS LECLERC ac. Lyon 1487-1508

JEAN DE SAINT-PRIEST ac. Lyon c. 1500

In 1500 the city of Lyon was visited by Louis XII and Anne of Brittany, and to celebrate the occasion presented the Royal couple with a splendid medal measuring about 4½ inches in diameter. The medal was modelled by Nicolas Leclerc (who in a document is referred to as "tailleur d'images" in 1499) and Jean de Saint-Priest. The casting was done by the brothers Jean and Colin Le Pere. The medal (no. 78), with its lingering touch of the Gothic, is one of the most admirable examples of French art from the waning Middle Ages.

78

Louis XII 1462-1515, King of France 1498-1515 and *Anne of Brittany* 1477-1514, Queen of France 1491-1514

Large bronze medal, 113 mm. diam., 1499

(crosslet) FELICE · LVDOVICO · REGNANTE · DVODECIMO · CESARE · ALTERO · GAVDET · OMNIS · NACIO · On a field sown with fleurs-de-lis, bust of Louis XII to right, wearing crown over cap, robe and collar of St. Michael; below, lion of Lyon.

Rev. (crosslet) LVGDVN(ensi) · REPVBLICA · GAVDE(n)TE · BIS · ANNA · REGNANTE · BENIGNE · SIC · FVI · CONFLATA · 1499. On a field sown with fleurs-de-lis and ermine, bust of Anne to left, crowned and veiled; below, lion of Lyon.

Hill, *Medals of the Renaissance,* pl. XXIV, 3
Hill, *Dreyfus Coll.,* no. 527, pl. CXIII
Friedlaender, p. 207, 1
Loebbecke Coll., Munich 1908, no. 24, pl. IV
Forrer, III, 364; IV, 454 (ill.); V, 303 (ill.)
Mazerolle, cf. no. 27
Rondot, p. 16
Rosenheim Coll., no. 554, pl. 24

Anne inherited Brittany in 1488 from her father, Francis II. Consequently her hand was eagerly sought by a number of suitors. Archduke Maximilian (later Emperor Maximilian I) in 1490 married her by proxy. The French, however, forced Anne to seek annulment of this marriage, and in 1491 she was married to Charles VIII with the stipulation that in case of his death she was to marry his successor. Accordingly, in 1499 she married Louis XII, who for the purpose had obtained a divorce from his first wife. These developments led to the eventual incorporation of Brittany into France.

Provenance: Count Trivulzio Coll.

ETIENNE DE LAUNE c. 1518-c. 1583

In his youth De Laune exercised the trade of goldsmith, modeller, and engraver. Cellini's work seems to have inspired some of his early productions, which are most graceful and pleasing. In 1552, upon the establishment by Henri II of the "Monnaie du Moulin," in which coins no longer were struck by hammer but by machine, De Laune was elected to the office of engraver. Several drawings by the artist's hand of medals, coins, etc., are preserved at the Bibliotheque Nationale.

78

Henry II 1519-59, King of France 1547-59

Bronze medal, 53 mm. diam.

HENRICVS · II · FRANCOR · REX · INVICTISS · P · P · Laureate bust right, wearing armor. Pearled border.

Rev. TE · COPIA · LAVRO · ET · FAMA · BEARVNT · NVIA Fama, holding trumpet, driving a quadriga to right in which Pax and Abundance are seated. Pearled border.

Forrer, III, 337
Armand, III, 285, D
Tresor, I, XI, 5
Mazerolle, no. 103

GERMAIN PILON c. 1535-90

Pilon takes his place among the eminent French sculptors and medallists of the second half of the sixteenth century. One of his masterpieces is the monument to Henri II and Catherine de Medici at St. Denis. His medallic productions are conspicuous for their very large size, a purely French fashion which has no equivalent elsewhere.

80

Henry III 1551-89, King of France 1574-89, elected King of Poland 1573

Bronze medal, 154 mm. diam., 1575

HENRICVS · 3 · D G · FRAN · ET · POL · REX 1575 Bust almost facing front, wearing soft beret ornamented with feathers and jewels, ruff collar, triple chain over brocaded gown.

No reverse.

Tresor, Med. Franc., pl. XXIV, 1
Babelon, no. 167
Forrer, IV, 542/3 (ill.)

GUILLAUME DUPRÉ c. 1574-c. 1643

During this celebrated artist's life the French medal found its highest technical achievement. Although Dupré's products may not rival those of the great Italian masters in their conception and composition, their execution is so fine, their details so delicate, that they are a source of continuous enjoyment.

Dupré was comptroller-general of the French mint from 1604-39, but his influence on coinage was negligible. He was one of the last representatives of the French Renaissance and one of France's greatest medallists.

81

Henry IV 1553-1610, King of France 1589-1610

Bronze medal, 57 mm. diam., 1604

HENRICVS · IIII · D · G · FRANC · ET · NAVAR · REX Laureate bust right, bearded, dressed as a Roman Emperor, wearing drapery over cuirass. Underneath: · 1604 ·

Rev. MAIESTAS · MAIOR · AB · IGNE · Henry IV and his wife Marie de Medici, shaking hands over a flaming altar. In the exergue: 1604.

Mazerolle, no. 283

Provenance: Loebbecke Coll., Halle 1925, no. 76, pl. VI

82

Marcantonio Memmo Doge of Venice 1612-15 and *Cardinal Maffeo Barberini* later Pope Urban VIII

Bronze medal, 91.5 mm. diam., 1612

MARCVS ANTONIVS MEMMO DVX VENETIARVM Bearded bust right, wearing brocaded dress and ducal hat. Under the truncation: G. DUPRE F · 1612 Pearled border.

Rev. MAPH · S · R · E · P · CAR · - BARBERIN · SIG · IVST · PRAE · BONO · LEG Bust with short beard to right, in ecclesiastical garb. Under the truncation: G. DUPRE · F · 1612 Pearled border.

Tresor, Med. Franc., 15, 3
Forrer, I, 657
Provenance: Dr. Benno Geiger Coll.

83

Marie de Medici 1573-1642, Queen of France 1600-31

Bronze medal, 63 mm. diam., 1615

MARIA AVG. GALLIAE ET NAVARAE REGINA Bust right, wearing diadem and earring, high lace collar closed with a cross on brocaded gown. Below truncation, artist's signature: G. DUPRE 1615. All in concave field. Pearled border.

Rev. SERVANDO DEA FACTA DEOS Marie in a ship manned by four girls. Above, two blowing zephyrs.

Tresor, Med. Franc., pl. V, 4
Mazerolle, no. 680
Lanna Coll., no. 411
Loebbecke Coll., no. 206 (Munich 1908)

Provenance: British Museum Duplicates (Sotheby, July 13, 1922, no. 39)

JEAN WARIN ac. 1627-c. 1672

Warin succeeded Jean Darmand, called Lorfelin, as engraver to the mint in 1646. Together with Dupré, Jean Warin holds a most honored place in the history of French medallic art. To this talented artist we owe some of France's most beautiful medals and coins of the seventeenth century. His medallic productions bear the mark of his highly developed technical skill and distinguish themselves by their boldness of relief.

Little is known about Warin's early life. He may have been born at Liege, but he settled in France in 1627 and was naturalized in 1650. He enjoyed the all-powerful protection of Cardinal Richelieu, whom he portrayed on several medals. Warin was working on a series of historic medals of Louis XIV when death cut his life short.

84

Armand Jean Du Plessis 1586-1642, Cardinal de Richelieu 1622-42
Silver medal, 77 mm. diam., 1630
· ARMANDVS IOANNES CARDINALIS DE RICHELIEV Bust with short beard in very high relief to right, wearing skullcap. Pearled border.

Rev. TANDEM VICTA SEQVOR Francia holding sword of justice and palm branch, seated in a quadriga, driven to left by Fama, who is blowing trumpet to which is attached a banner with the coat of arms of Richelieu. Fortuna is chained to the back of the quadriga, while Victory is flying overhead, crowning Francia. Under curved exerguel line: · I · WARIN · | · 1630 · Pearled border.

Tresor, Med. Franc., XXI, 3
Loebbecke Coll., no. 215 (bronze)
Gallet Coll., no. 166 (bronze)
Forrer, VI, 369

Hill, *Medals of the Renaissance,* p. 148, writes: "Jean's portrait of Richelieu is brilliant in its bold handling of the relief," pl. XXVI, 7 (British Museum specimen, bronze with the date removed)
Bernhart, *Medaillen und Plaketten,* p. 33

BERTINET seventeenth century, worked for Louis XIV

85

Michel Le Tellier 1603-85, French statesman, Minister under Louis XIV and Mazarin, later Chancellor of France
Bronze medal, 132 mm. diam., 1678
MICHA (rosette) LETELLIER (rosette) FR (rosette) CANCELLARIVS (rosette) 1678 On granulated band. Bust right, wearing robe, skullcap and decoration, all within a laurel wreath.
No reverse.

GERMAN MEDALS

ALBRECHT DÜRER 1471-1528
Only a few medals have been attributed to Dürer, but a number of others as well as some plaquettes are based on his designs. An outstanding example is a plaquette of *The Entombment* (no. 184).

86

Lucretia, formerly described as Agnes Dürer, the artist's wife
Lead medal, 55 mm. diam., 1508
Female head with open flowing hair, slightly inclined to left, almost facing front. In the field, to the left: 1508; to the right, the Dürer monogram: D within A.
No reverse.
Habich, *Corpus,* I, 1; no. 14, pl. II, 2; and fig. 5
Lanna Coll., no. 908, pl. 42
Will, p. 369
Sallet, p. 25
Sallet, *Zeitschrift f. Numismatik,* II, 362
Erman, pl. I, 1
Merzbacher Coll., 1914, no. 37
Paris, *Cabinet des Medailles,* fig. 5
Provenance: Dr. Jacob Hirsch Estate

CHRISTOPH WEIDITZ ac. 1523-c. 1533
A native of Strassburg, Weiditz settled in Augsburg in 1526, and from there made various trips abroad. He modelled his Cortez medal in Spain in 1529.

Weiditz, like many other of his contemporaries, carved the models for his medals in boxwood. Many of his portraits show a marked affinity in style to those of Hans Holbein the Younger.

87

Hernan Cortez 1485-1547
Bronze medal, 56 mm. diam., 1529
DON · FERDINANDO · CORTES · MD · XXIX · ANNO · ETATIS · XXXXII · Bust facing front, slightly turned towards the right, with long hair and short, straight-cut beard, wearing loose gown and flat biretta.

Rev. IVDICIVM · DNI · APPREHENDIT · EOS | ET · FORTITVDO · EIVS | CORROBORAVIT | BRACHIVM · MEVM Divine arm issuing from clouds.

Habich, *Corpus*, I, 1, no. 376, pl. XLIX, 4
Domanig, *Deutsche Medaille*, no. 100
Berlin, *Amtliche Berichte*, p. 52
Babelon, XIV, 6

FRIEDRICH HAGENAUER ac. c. 1525-46

Hagenauer was one of the most prolific of the classical German medallists. Born at Strassburg, he settled in Augsburg in 1527. His success aroused the jealousy of the guild of painters and sculptors of Augsburg, and since he was not a member of the guild, they attempted to restrict his activity. He contended, however, that medallic art was a free art, and therefore not subject to guild law. It would appear that the guild won out, for by 1532 he was working again in Strassburg.

Hagenauer was an efficient craftsman and his medals portray the sitter with remarkable precision. Great care is taken to show every detail of face and dress. Although a sculptor as well, he is known mainly as a medallist and, in his own terms, "sought to earn his bread as a medallist."

88

Unknown Humanist (in the past tentatively identified as Menno van Friesland 1492-1559)

Silver medal, 56 mm. diam.

Bust facing left, wearing beret and ecclesiastical gown. Granulated field.

Rev. Later engraving: D. MARTINUS. LUTHERUS. Open Bible on altar.

Habich, *Corpus*, I, 1, no. 633, pl. LXXVIII, 11
Van Mieris, II, 251
Juncker, p. 535
Lanna Coll., III, no. 1211, pl. 50

According to Habich, this medal dates from about 1539.

89

Philipp Melanchthon 1497-1560, Reformation leader and humanist

Bronze medal, 38 mm. diam., 1543

PHILIPPVS · MELANTHON · ANNO · AETATIS · SVAE · XLVII Bust left, bareheaded and bearded with long hair, wearing gown. In the field, artist's signature: FH.

Rev. In five lines: PSAL · 36 | SVBDITVS ESTO | DEO ET ORA EVM | ANNO · | M. D. XXXXIII.

Habich, *Corpus*, I, 1, no. 651, pl. LXXX, 1
Juncker, p. 145
Tresor, Med. All., XVI, 3
Lanna Coll., III, no. 930
Loebbecke Coll., Amsterdam 1929, no. 246, pl. XVII

JOACHIM DESCHLER ac. 1540-c. 1569

Although Deschler spent two years as a student in Italy, his medallic pro-

ductions are thoroughly German in every respect. A typical example is the extraordinary portrait of the well-nourished, Nürnberg sexton, Hieronymus Paumgartner, which possesses all the realism so characteristic of German medallic art (no. 90).

Little is known about Deschler's place of birth. He became a Nürnberg citizen in 1537, attended various "Reichstag" sessions in order to practice his art there, and worked for Archduke Maximilian, the future Emperor. In the latter part of 1550 he went to Vienna and entered into the permanent employ of the art-loving Emperor, who raised him to the rank of "Imperial sculptor."

90

Hieronymus Paumgartner 1497-1565, Nürnberg church-warden

Bronze medal, 66.5 mm. diam., 1553

HIERONYMVS · PAVMGARTNER · ANNO · AETATIS · 56 · Bust front, bald-headed and with side-whiskers, wearing gown over loose shirt. All within border of leaves. On truncation: 1553.

Rev. IN · VMBRA · ALARVM · TVARVM · SPERABO · DONEC · TRANSEAT · INIQVITAS · Helmeted coat of arms on drapery. Border of leaves.

Habich, *Corpus*, I, 2, no. 1611, pl. CLXXIII, 7
Imhof, 608, 3
Koehler, XV, 137
Tresor, Med. All., pl. III, 10
Loebbecke Coll., Munich 1908, no. 297, pl. XIX
Lanna Coll., III, no. 1015, pl. 45
Rosenheim Coll., no. 433
Provenance: Dr. Jacob Hirsch Estate

Johann Neudoerfer 1497-1563, "Schreib-und Rechenmeister" in Nürnberg

Silver medal with old fire-gilding, 24 mm. diam., 1554

IOHANN : NEVDORFFER · ARITHM : AET: SVE. LVII Bust right, with long hair, wearing gown with small ruffled collar. Pearled border. On truncation: 1554.

Rev. INDVSTRIAM · ADIVVAT · DEVS Helmeted coat of arms. Pearled border.

Habich, *Corpus*, I, 2, no. 1617, pl. CLXXIV, 4
Imhof, 849, 8
Tresor, Med. All., pl. XXXII, I
Domanig, *Jahrbuch* (Vienna), XIV, 32, no. 22, pl. V
Frankfurter Münzzeitung, 1903, p. 496, pl. 22, 8
Felix Coll., no. 187
Loebbecke Coll., Munich 1908, no. 305, pl. XX
Lanna Coll., III, no. 1016, pl. 45
Domanig, *Deutsche Medaille*, no. 162

JOACHIM DESCHLER, SCHOOL OF

92

Frederick Von Wirsberg Bishop of Würzburg 1558-73

Silver medal with old fire-gilding, 27 mm. diam., 1572

FRIDERICVS · D · G · EPS · WIRCEBVRG · Bust facing three-quarters right, with long hair, wearing biretta, fur-lined cloak over gown, and jewelled chain. In the field: 15 - 7Z.

Rev. AETATIS · SVAE · 65 · FRANCIAE ORIENTALIS DVX · Under three helmets, the quadripartite shield.

Habich, *Corpus*, I, 2, no. 1682, pl. CLXXXI, I
L. & L. Hamburger, 1891, no. 1200

Provenance: Vogel Coll., no. 140, pl. 15

MICHAEL HOHENAUER, first half of the sixteenth century

Probably a native of Prague, he held a variety of positions at the mint in his home town and in Vienna. The artist's date of death is believed to have been about 1558.

93

Louis II 1506-26, King of Hungary 1516-26, and *his wife Maria*, sister of Charles V

Silver medal, with old fire-gilding, 41 mm. diam., 1526

LVDOVIC · VNGA · EC · REX · CONTRA · TVRCA · PVGNANDO · OCCVBVIT · Bust left, with long hair and short beard, wearing broad-rimmed hat, fur-lined mantle over pleated gown, and the sash with the Golden Fleece. In the field: · 1 · 5 · - Z6 | ETATIS - SVE · 30 ·

Rev. MARIA · REGINA · EC · QVOS · DEVS · CONIVNXIT · HOMO · NON · SEPERET · Bust left, wearing wire cap and double necklace over bodice.

Habich, *Corpus*, II, 1; compare no. 1897, pl. CCI, I (her bust to right)
Lanna Coll., III, no. 659
Donebauer Coll., no. 980
Forrer, II, 518 (ill.): "Fiala considers this medal as the artist's best production; it is executed with special care and is a remarkable piece of workmanship, of characteristic style."

Louis (Lajos) II was the last of the Jagiello Dynasty, ruling the two kingdoms of Hungary and Bohemia. In the Battle of Mohacs, 1526, commemorated by this medal, his army was utterly destroyed and he was killed by the Turks under Suleiman I, who used artillery in open battle for the first time in history. Through a marriage treaty concluded by his father Wladislas II, the crowns of Hungary and Bohemia passed to Louis's brother-in-law, Ferdinand of Hapsburg, resulting in the union which was to last four centuries between Hungary, Bohemia, and the Hapsburg lands.

HANS REINHART THE ELDER ac. c. 1530-80

Probably one of the best-known Renaissance medallists of the Saxonian School.

Reinhart's hallmark is the technique of casting various portions of the medal separately and, by soldering, joining them onto the design, in order to achieve a three-dimensional effect. An example of this method are the leaves of the Tree of Wisdom on the *Fall of Man* medal (no. 95). Reinhart's extraordinary technical skill won him great praise. His products are considered masterpieces of craftsmanship.

In 1539 Reinhart settled in Leipzig. Prior to that time, he may have been a pupil of Lucas Cranach, whose influence is apparent in his work.

94

John Frederick Elector of Saxony 1532-37

Silver medal, 66 mm. diam., 1535

IOANNS · FRIDERICVS · ELECTOR · DVX · SAXONIE · FIERI · FE-CIT · ETATIS · SVAE · 32 Bearded half-bust almost facing front, holding the electoral sword and hat; wearing necklace and fur cloak over loose gown, the collar of which is embroidered: REN ALS IN EREN ·

Rev. SPES · MEA · IN · DEO · EST · ANNO · NOSTRI · SALVATO-RIS · M · D · X · X · X · V Triple-helmeted large coat of arms with the electoral shield (two crossed swords) in the center.

Habich, *Corpus*, II, 1, no. 1935, pl. CCIV, 3 and 3a
Tentzel, *Ernestine Line*, pl. 7, I
Domanig, *Deutsche Medaille*, no. 154
Loebbecke Coll., Munich 1908, no. 562, pl. XXXI
Lanna Coll., III, no. 861, pl. 40

The portrait on this medal is based on a woodcut by Lucas Cranach (Gotha Landesmuseum), made about 1533 (cf. Geisberg, *Einblattholzschnitte*, no. XIII, 14).

95

Fall of Man | *Crucifixion*

Silver medal, 68.5 mm. diam., 1536

ET · SICVT · IN · ADAM · OMNES · MORIVNTVR · ITA · ET · IN · CHRISTVM · OMNES VIVIFICABVNTVR · VNVS · QVISQVE · IN · ORDINE · SVO · Adam and Eve, surrounded by the animals of Paradise including a unicorn, under the Tree of Wisdom, the foliage of which is soldered to the medal (typical of Reinhart's early work). In the background, left, the creation of Eve; right, the expulsion from Paradise. In the left field the electoral shield of Saxony, in the right, the ducal shield. Underneath, on a ribbon: IOANNS · FRIDERICVS · ELECTOR · DVX · SAXONIE · FIERI · FECIT

Rev. VT · MOSES · EREXIT · SERPETE · ITA · CHRS · IN · CRVCE · EXALTATVS · ET · RESVSCITATVS · CAPVT · SERPENTIS · CON-TRIVIT · SALVARET · CREDENTES · Christ on the cross between the two thieves. Below, Mary, St. John, and mercenaries. In the background, left, the Church; right, the Resurrection. Under the cross, the artist's signature: H R and 1536. Below, on a ribbon: SPES · MEA · IN · DEO · EST ·

Habich, *Corpus*, II, 1, no. 1968, pl. CCXI, I, 3 and 4
Tentzel, *Ernestine Line*, pl. VIII, I
Domanig, *Deutsche Medaille*, no. 762

Lanna Coll., III, no. 1290, pl. 53
Loebbecke Coll., Munich 1908, no. 567, pl. xxxi
Van Mieris, II, 447
Mueller-Lebanon Coll., no. 88, pl. IX
Forrer, V, pp. 78, 79 (ill.)
Provenance: Dr. Jacob Hirsch Estate

96

Fall of Man | Crucifixion

Silver medal, with old fire-gilding, 56 mm. diam.

Similar to the last, but without the circular legends. In the obverse field: MVLIER · DEDIT · MIHI · ET · COMEDI · GE · Z · In the reverse field: MISERERE · NOBIS · DOMINE

Habich, *Corpus,* II, I, no. 1969, pl. ccviii, 2
Tentzel, *Ernestine Line,* pl. 8, II
Lanna Coll., III, no. 1288, pl. 53
Loebbecke Coll., Munich 1908, no. 569, pl. xxxi

VALENTIN MALER c. 1568-1603

A native of Moravia, Maler's chief center of activity for 35 years was Nürnberg. He was the son-in-law of the famous Nürnberg goldsmith, Wenzel Jamnitzer. Thanks to this relationship, he obtained by special favor of the Nürnberg Town Council the privileges of a mastership.

The number of medals by the artist's hand is most impressive; yet in spite of his diligence he died a poor man, leaving his widow 1100 gulden in debt. His house was inherited by his son Christian, along with its un-paid mortgage of 1900 gulden.

97

Matthaeus Fetzer 1527-83, Nürnberg Councilman 1556

Silver medal, 29 mm. diam., 1576

MATHEVS FETZER · AET : LI 1576 Bearded bust, three-quarters facing right, wearing gown with high ruff collar.

Rev. ALL MEIN HOFNVNG ZV GOT Helmeted coat of arms, surrounded by three smaller shields.

Habich, *Corpus,* II, I, no. 2509; pl. ccli, 6
Will, IV, 299
Binder, 573, 20
Delbecke Coll., no. 822
Provenance: Trau Coll., no. 1761, pl. IX
         Gallet Coll., no. 105, pl. X

GEORG HOLDERMANN Nürnberg 1585-1629

A goldsmith, medallist, and wax modeller, Holdermann's medallic work dates from between 1610 and 1629. He also seems to have been con-nected with the production of coins, as evidenced by a Nürnberg Council ordinance of 1620.

98

Philipp Adolf von Ehrenberg Bishop of Würzburg 1623-31

Oval silver medal with old fire-gilding, H. 37 mm., W. 31.5 mm., 1623

PHILIPP : ADOLPH : D · G : EPS WIRCEB · FR · OR · DVX Bust three-quarters to right, bareheaded and with long hair, square-cut beard and moustache, wearing broad-collared brocaded gown, buttoned in center.

Rev. Without legend. Helmeted shield, quadripartite with the coats of arms of Ehrenberg and the Diocese of Würzburg; above, 1623. Original suspension loop.

Habich, *Corpus,* II, I, no. 2799, pl. cclxxiv, 3
Schulthess-Rechberg Coll., no. 2832

GEORG HOLDERMANN, SCHOOL OF

99

Hugo Donellus (Doneau) 1527-91, famed law scholar

Oval lead medal, H. 52 mm., W. 40 mm., 1590

· HVGO · DONELLVS · IC · CL · PROF · ALDORP · AET · SVAE · 64 · AN · 90 · Bust facing front, in very high relief, wearing skullcap, ruff collar, and coat with fur collar over buttoned gown.

No reverse.

Habich, *Corpus,* II, I, no. 2807, pl. cclxxiv, 12
Will, III, no. 401, f
Koehler, VII, 385
Mazzuchelli, I, pl. xcv, 7
Domanig, *Deutsche Medaille,* no. 245
Imhof, II, 715, no. 21

UNIDENTIFIED ARTISTS

NÜRNBERG(?), SIXTEENTH CENTURY

100

Portrait of a Patrician

Oval wax medallion, H. 95 mm., W. 72 mm.

Portrait of a Nürnberg patrician almost facing front, with short hair and long broad beard, wearing black embroidered coat with white ruff collar.

In contemporary fire-gilded bronze case, adorned with fruit volutes, elaborate scrollwork with putto in center. Outside case height: 157 mm.; width: 90 mm.

Habich, *Corpus,* II, I, no. 2820 (this specimen)
Sonderausstellung catalogue, 1939/40, Kunstmuseum Bern, no. 42 (ill.) (this specimen)
Provenance: Spitzer Coll., Paris 1890, V, p. 191, no. 10
         Spitzer Coll., London 1893, II, no. 2959, pl. LVI
         Lanna Coll., Prague
         Pick Coll., Budapest
         Delmar Coll., Budapest

SOUTH GERMAN c. 1530

101

Anna von Frundsberg Countess of Lodron

Checker, ground marble on light wood, 50 mm. diam.

ANNA · GEORGI · IN · FRVNTSPERG · VXOR Bust left, wearing widow's veil (her husband died in 1527) and wide gown over pleated bodice.

cf. Habich, *Jahrbuch* 28, 1907, pl. J 8
cf. *Lanna Coll.*, II, no. 65, pl. 9

A wooden medal by Friedrich Hagenauer with Anna's portrait is recorded in Habich, *Corpus*, I, 1, no. 541, ill. 101.

102

Emerentiana von Tannhausen married 1521

Checker, ground marble on light wood, 50 mm. diam.

Bust, three-quarters facing, wearing pleated bonnet with plain wide border, cloak with shoulder collar over bodice.

cf. Habich, *Jahrbuch* 28, 1907, pl. J 8
cf. *Lanna Coll.*, II, no. 65, pl. 9

For portrait, cf. Habich, *Corpus*, I, 2, no. 1315, pl. CXLVIII, 1

103

Sybille of Saxony married 1527, d. 1554

Checker, ground marble on light wood, 50 mm. diam.

SIBILA · IOHANNI · FRIDERICHI · DVCIS · VXOR · SAXONIAE Bust three-quarters facing, wearing wire cap, necklace with pendant, gown with pleated sleeves over bodice.

cf. Habich, *Jahrbuch* 28, 1907, pl. J 8
cf. *Lanna Coll.*, II, no. 65, pl. 8

104

Euphrosina de Chamemilon

Checker, ground marble on light wood, 50 mm. diam.

EVPHROSINA · DE · CHAMEMILON Bust facing left, wearing bonnet with round ornament in center, necklace with pendant, and cloak over embroidered bodice.

cf. Habich, *Jahrbuch* 28, 1907, pl. J 8
cf. *Lanna Coll.*, II, no. 65, pl. 9

105

Frederick Behaim von Schwarzbach 1491-1533, Nürnberg Councilman

Checker, ground marble on ebony, 50 mm. diam.

Bust right, with beard and moustache, wearing wire cap and mantle with broad shoulder collar over high-closed, pleated gown.

cf. *Lanna Coll.*, II, no. 66, pl. 8
For portrait, cf. Habich, *Corpus*, I, 2, no. 936, pl. CXIV, 10.

106

Portrait of a Patrician (probably Wolfgang Vitil, Augsburg 1495-1540)

Checker, ground marble on ebony, 50 mm. diam.

Bust, three-quarters facing, with moustache and square beard, wearing brocaded coat over gown, and round wire cap.

cf. *Lanna Coll.*, II, no. 66, pl. 8
For portrait, cf. Habich, *Corpus*, I, 1, no. 485, pl. LXIV, 7.

107

Portrait of a Humanist (possibly Johann Caesarius, Ph.D. and M.D., born Juelich 1468)

Checker, ground marble on ebony, 50 mm. diam.

Bust, three-quarters facing, with long hair and beard, wearing scholastic gown and hat.

cf. *Lanna Coll.*, II, no. 66, pl. 8

Caesarius is portrayed on a medal, dated 1543, recorded in Habich, *Corpus*, I, 1, no. 661, pl. LXXXI, 8.

108

Portrait of an Unknown Mohammedan (probably a Turkish grand vizier)

Checker, ground marble on ebony, 50 mm. diam.

Bust right, wearing turban, earring, mantle with embroidered shoulder collar over pleated gown.

cf. *Lanna Coll.*, II, no. 66, pl. 8

SOUTH GERMAN, 1556

109

Hieronymus Allgaeuer b. 1509

Kehlheim stone model, 42 mm. diam., 1556 (in wooden frame)

HIERONYMVS · ALLGOEWER · XVIIL · IAR · ALT · A · MDLVI · Bearded bust facing front, bareheaded, wearing fur-lined coat with high collar turned down. Around the neck, a chain with medallion.

Provenance: Merzbacher Coll., Munich 1900, no. 346, pl. III
Neuburg Coll., no. 168, pl. XXII

BALDUIN DRENTWETT c. 1545-1627

Frisian by birth, Drentwett's home was in Augsburg from the early seventies, although he travelled widely in the practice of his art. He is assumed to have employed a considerable number of assistants, including some of lesser renown and ability. After 1612, Drentwett's productivity lessened, though several medals from the years 1612 to 1620 may still have come from his workshop.

110

Georg Mylius born in Augsburg 1548 (as Georg Miler), Professor of Theology in Wittenberg, d. 1607

Bronze medal with old gilding, 41 mm. diam.

D · GEORGIVS MYLIVS · AVG AET · 31 Bust with moustache and small pointed beard, almost facing front, wearing high-closed robe with ruff collar; granulated field. Cable border.

Rev. D · MARTINVS LVTERVS Bust of Luther three-quarters right; granulated field. Cable border.

Habich, *Corpus*, II, 1, no. 2943
Delbecke Coll., no. 864
Loebbecke Coll., Munich 1908, no. 369
Rosenheim Coll., no. 464
Archiv, 4 (1913/14), p. 188, pl. XV, 10

The reverse of this medal is by Valentin Maler, and was copied by Drentwett. Habich dates the medal c. 1579.

111

Charles I 1560-1600, Count Palatine 1569-1600

Gold medal, 23.5 mm. diam., 1591

CAR · D · G · CO · PA · RHE · BA · DV · C · V · E · S Bareheaded bust with short beard and moustache, three-quarters facing right, wearing ruff collar and double chain.

Rev. ANNO DO MI MDXCI Minerva standing on a book, holding a palm branch and crowning Patientia who caresses a lamb; at her feet a mirror.

Habich, *Corpus,* II, 1, no. 2991, pl. CCLXXXVII, 3
Exter, II, 144, no. 102
Spiess, IV, 363
Streber, p. 7, fig. 1

ANTONIO ABONDIO 1538-91

Abondio was of Lombard, perhaps Milanese, origin. His father, Alessandro Abondio, was a celebrated wax modeller during the first half of the sixteenth century, and a pupil of Michelangelo. It was the elder Abondio who introduced young Antonio into the art of modelling and undoubtedly imparted much of his genius to his son.

In 1565 Antonio left his native land and travelled across the Alps. A year later we find him in the employ of Emperor Maximilian II, whom the artist portrayed on a number of medals. With the exception of occasional visits to The Netherlands, Spain, Bavaria, and Northern Italy, Antonio spent nearly all of his life in Prague and Vienna.

Upon the death of Maximilian, Rudolf II secured the artist's services and, like his father, continued to bestow many favors on him.

wearing armor, coat, and the sash of the Golden Fleece. In the lower left field, the artist's signature: AN:AB:

Rev. Mounted St. George, helmeted and bearded, galloping to right, spearing the dragon.

Habich, *Corpus,* II, 2, 3412 note (this specimen described and illustrated)
Archiv 3/4 (1921/22), p. 91

Dr. V. Katz in *Berliner Münzblaetter,* 1930, p. 17 (this specimen described and illustrated): "A work by Antonio Abondio, hitherto unknown, which is different from the other reverses of his medals, but which does not hide the artistic hand of this master. The bearded representation of St. George, usually shown as a young man, is perhaps connected with the portrait of the Emperor on the obverse. The medal is undated, but is close to the one on Johann Khevenhueller (Fiala no. 25, pl. III, 3), made around 1571. Minerva on the reverse of that medal wears a similar armor as St. George here. As Maximilian's portrait also appears on another medal together with that of Maria dated 1575 (Fiala no. 38, pl. II, 3), this present Maximilian medal with the St. George reverse originated probably between the years 1571 and 1575. The tinsmith, Caspar Enderlein, has used this St. George design by Abondio on a tin plate (illustrated in H. Demiani, *Francois Briot, Caspar Enderlein, and the Tin,* Leipzig 1897)."

Unique.

Provenance: Dr. Viktor Katz Coll.

113

Maximilian II

Antonio Abondio occupies a rank of honor among the medallists of his age. His medals show a blend of Italian and German art.

112

Maximilian II of Hapsburg 1527-76, Emperor 1564-76

Silver medal with old fire-gilding, 61 mm. diam., 1575, in frame with three chains ending in one ring. The frame has the Viennese inspection stamp used from the end of the sixteenth century to 1674 (Rosenberg no. 5065) and the monogram AL.

IMP:CAES: MAXIMIL:II:AVG: Bust right, bareheaded and bearded,

Silver medal, 24.5 mm. diam., 1570

· MAXIMILI · II · ROM I S AV Bearded and laureate bust left, wearing ruff collar, armor and drapery, and the sash with the Golden Fleece.

Rev. · DOMINVS · 15 - 70 · PROVIDEBIT · Facing eagle with spread wings holding a globe.

Habich, *Corpus,* II, 2, no. 3438, pl. CCCXXI, 9
Lanna Coll., III, no. 721
Loebbecke Coll., Munich 1908, no. 560

.. Hamburger, 1922, no. 136
Herrgott, III, pl. IX, 41
Donebauer Coll., no. 1232

PAULUS VAN VIANEN ac. c. 1592-1612

Born at or near Utrecht into a family of artists, together with his brother Adam, Paulus received his early training from his father, an able goldsmith, and a certain Cornelius Elertz of Munich. Thereafter he continued to develop his talents in Rome. He was falsely denounced to the Inquisition and imprisoned for several months.

Upon his release, about 1596, Paulus left for Munich where, according to a record in the goldsmiths' annals, he was received as "Master" in 1599. In 1603, the artist's services were secured by Emperor Rudolf II, for a monthly salary of twenty gulden (most other artists in the Imperial employ received only ten gulden). His principal works belong to this Imperial period in Prague.

Paulus van Vianen's products have been compared to those of Cellini because of their excellence of workmanship and finish. The artist died of the plague in 1613.

114

Rudolf II of Hapsburg 1552-1612, Emperor 1576-1612

Oval silver medal with old fire-gilding, H. 38 mm., W. 46 mm.

RVDOLPHVS II ROM IMP AVG REX HVNG BOE Bearded bust facing front, wearing laurel wreath, cuirass, ruff collar and sash with the order of the Golden Fleece.

Rev. FIRMAVIT OMEN Capricorn over globe; above, the Hapsburg eagle winging toward the sun.

Original loop for wearing. Hung with pearl.

Habich, *Corpus,* II, 2, no. 3555 (this specimen)

Provenance: Trau Coll., no. 615, pl. III
           Belli Coll., no. 6389

Unique.

UNIDENTIFIED ARTIST, SIXTEENTH CENTURY

115

Louis VI Count Palatine 1576-83

Silver medal with old gilding, H. 35 mm., W. 31 mm., 1580

LVD · D · G · CO · PA · ELE · A · D · Z · Bareheaded and bearded bust right, wearing ruff collar and drapery. Pearled border.

Rev. VINCES · VIRTVTE · VIVENTIS · 1580 The Resurrection. Pearled border. Suspension loop.

Exter, I, 58, no. 51

RUPRECHT NICLAS KITZKATZ Dresden, ac. c. 1615-33

116

Sophia of Brandenburg 1568-1622, wife of Christian I, Elector of Saxony

Oval silver medal, H. 39 mm., W. 30 mm., 1622

D : G : SOPHIA · NAT : MAR : BRAN : DVC SAX · ELE : Veiled bust left, wearing ruff collar and jewel on triple chain.

Rev. SEREN · D · D · IOH · GEORG · ELECT · SAX · IN · MATR · CHARISS · In the field, under an angel's head: NAT: 6 JUN : | 1568 | MOR: 7 DEC: | 1622 | PIETAS

Schulthess-Rechberg Coll., no. 4688
Loebbecke Coll., Munich 1908, no. 698, pl. XXXV
Tentzel, pl. XXII, 9
Berlin, *Amtliche Berichte,* no. 78
Engelhardt, no. 420

SEBASTIAN DADLER ac. 1619-54

A goldsmith and a foremost medallist of the seventeenth century, Dadler was born at Strassburg, but was active chiefly at Augsburg, Nürnberg, Hamburg, and Dresden. At Augsburg he held the title of "First Goldsmith to the Imperial Court," and there attained considerable celebrity.

At a later stage in his career, Dadler worked for the Electoral Court of Saxony, where he executed various articles of plate in repoussé work for John George I. So great was Dadler's reputation, that many princely houses of Europe eagerly tried to enlist his services. The latter part of his life was spent at Dresden, where he died, presumably in 1654.

117

Christ and St. Paul

Silver medal, 43 mm. diam., 1625

(italics) CHRISTUM HAT GOTT FURGESTELT ZU EINEM GNADENSTUEL The Savior, haloed, wearing the crown of thorns. To the left, a mercenary; to the right, St. Paul. Underneath: 1625.

Rev. (italics) JESUS HAT SICH ZUM LOSEGELT BEIM HIMLISCHEN VATTER DARGESTELT FUR ALLE SUND DER GANTZEN WELT within foliate wreath. Underneath, the artist's signature: S - D ·

118

Frederick III 1609-70, King of Denmark 1648-70

Oval silver medal, H. 58 mm., W. 48 mm., 1648

FRIDERICUS III. D G. DAN. NORW. GOT. VAND REX. DUX SL. HOLST. DIT. COM. IN OLD. & DELM. Within a baroque cartouche, the King's bust, three-quarters facing, wearing wig, lace collar, drapery over cuirass, with lion's head on shoulder, on the breast the Order of the Elephant. Below, the artist's initials: S - D and 16 - 48.

Rev. SEHT WIE DER FRIED IEZ ZIERT DIE WELT DA FRIDRICH KROHN UND SCEPTER HELT On a pedestal Pax seated, holding the raying Sun, palm branch and an open book inscribed: DAS HOEHESTE GUT, her feet resting on a globe.

Danske Mynter og Medailler, pl. I, no. 5
Domanig, *Deutsche Medaille,* no. 329

Commemorates the King's accession and the conclusion of the Peace of Westphalia.

SEBASTIAN DADLER, SCHOOL OF

119

Christ Showing the Stigmata

Silver medal, 36 mm. diam., 1625

VULNER - CHRISTI Christ, wearing the crown of thorns, showing the stigmata. Below: 1625.

Rev. NOSTRA MEDELA Winged archangel, carrying the cross. In the background, rooster on column.

JOHANN JAKOB KORNMANN also known as GIOVANNI JACOPO CORMANO first half of the seventeenth century

Kornmann was born in Augsburg, but his enthusiasm led him to Italy, where he italianized his name. He worked with great success at Venice and Rome. It was his misfortune to fall into the hands of the Inquisition at Rome and thus lose his goods and liberty. The style and the finish of his medals are of great precision.

Christian William of Brandenburg 1587-1665, Archbishop of Magdeburg and Halberstadt

Oval silver medal, H. 41 mm., W. 31 mm., 1627

V G G C W P A B E V·S M : V H P : G M Z B I P H (Von Gottes Gnaden, Christian Wilhelm, Postulierter Administrator beider Erz- Und Stift Magdeburg Und Halberstadt, Primas Germaniae, Markgraf Zu Brandenburg, In Preussen Herzog). Bearded bust, three-quarters facing, bareheaded, wearing lace collar and drapery over cuirass. Underneath: 1627

Rev. In four lines: THVE RECHT | FVRCHTE GOTT | VND NIEMANTS | MEHR

Suspension loop.

Berlin, *Amtliche Berichte,* p. 43, no. 111, pl. 13 (specimen from the H. Hauswaldt Coll.)

This is the second recorded specimen.

UNIDENTIFIED ARTISTS, SEVENTEENTH CENTURY

121

Gustav II Adolf 1594-1632, King of Sweden 1611-32

Silver medal, 63 mm. diam., 1629

GVSTAVVS ADOLP: D:G: SVEC: GOTH: WAND: Q: REX. Laureate bust with pointed beard and moustache, three-quarters facing right, wearing lace collar and military sash over cuirass. Broad foliate border.

Rev. In six lines, arranged in the shape of the divine eye: DEVM COLE | AVRVM CONTEMNE | VIRTVTEM SECTARE | ARGENTVM SPERNE | PATRIAM DEFENDE | 16Z9, all under the glorified name of God in Hebrew letters. Broad foliate border.

Hildebrand, I, no. 73
Oldenburg Coll., no. 359
Schultze Coll., no. 82

Commemorates his victories in the Thirty Years' War.

Provenance: Crona Coll., no. 75

122

Gustav II Adolf

Oval bronze medal, H. 45 mm., W. 27 mm., 1629

GVSTAVVS ADOLP : D : G : SVEC : GOTH : WAND : Q : REX Laureate bust to right, with short beard, wearing lace collar and drapery over cuirass.

Rev. The Hebrew name of God ET VICTRICIBVS ARMIS ("Deo et victricibus armis" was the motto of Gustav Adolf.) Religion and Svecia standing at a column, between anchor and lion (referring to the King's successful landing in Germany).

Hildebrand, I, no. 87
Provenance: Crona Coll., no. 81

123

Ferdinand III of Hapsburg 1608-57, Emperor 1637-57, Victor of the Battle of Noerdlingen 1634

Silver medal with old fire-gilding, 56 mm. diam., c. 1634-36

FERD. III. D. G. ROM. HVNG. BOHEM. R. ARCHID. AVSTR. DVX. BVRGV. LVCENBVRG. SILES: STYR. CARINT. CARN. WIRTENB. MARCHIO. MORA. LVSAT. COMES. HABSP. TIROL: EC (title as King of the Romans, Hungarians, Bohemians, etc., thus before his election as Emperor, 1637). Within double circle of legend, two putti hold crown over a medallion surrounded by the chain of the Golden Fleece, showing Ferdinand, bareheaded, with long hair and pointed beard, wearing lace collar and drapery over cuirass.

Rev. QVAMVIS OCCVMBAS · FELIX OCCVMBIS : IN IPSO STARE TVAM EFFIGIEM. SOL ORIENTE VIDES On a river in a mountainous landscape, over which the sun rises, haloed St. Peter guides his boat through the waves; before him, on the Bible the crossed keys and the Papal tiara; the Hapsburg eagle perched on the sceptre. Above, SERENITATIS NVNCIA. Suspension loop.

This medal commemorates the short-lived Hapsburg successes in the Thirty Years' War. After Ferdinand's election as Emperor, things took a turn for the worse, until Ferdinand had to assent to the Peace of Westphalia, 1648.

JOHANN BLUM ac. 1631-60

A resident of Bremen, Blum made a number of medals for the Houses of Saxony, Brunswick, and Orange.

124

Bernhard of Saxe-Weimar 1604-39

Silver medal, 53 mm. diam., 1638

HEROIS HUIUS NOMINA IN CUNCTA CLARENT SECULA. Within an elaborate baroque cartouche, bust of Bernhard, three-quarters facing left, wearing cuirass, lace collar and sash, and holding staff. Around (in italics) Magni ducis Bernhardi Saxon. Weim. effigies. Under the cartouche, the artist's signature: Blum.

Rev. BRISACH FORTIS SED FORTIOR DEUS FVIT ET WEIMARIUS · 1638 · View of the city of Breisach across the Rhine, showing its system of fortifications.

Tentzel, pl. xxxix, 3
Reimmann Coll., no. 6372
Forrer, I, 201

Commemorates Bernhard's capture of Breisach.

Provenance: Crona Coll., no. 189

JOHANN BARTHOLOMAEUS BRAUN Nürnberg ac. c. 1636-66

The artist was married to Anna Maria Pfruendt, the daughter of another well-known medallist, and a medallist in her own right.

125

Sigmund Gabriel Holzschuher 1575-1642, Nürnberg Councilman 1606

Lead medal, 51 mm. diam., 1642

SIGM:GABRIEL HOLZSCHVHER · AE: 67 · Bust three-quarters facing right, bareheaded with square-cut beard, wearing large ruff collar and gown. The portrait realistically shows a large wart on the forehead.

Rev. SPE GLORIAE HVMILIS Helmeted shield, to the sides, 16-42.

Forrer, I, 269/270
Lanna Coll., III, no. 1123, pl. 48
Loebbecke Coll., Munich 1908, no. 625
Felix Coll., no. 136 (probably this specimen)
Imhof, p. 394, 14
Will, II, 305

JOHANN BUCHHEIM 1624-83

Buchheim worked for Bishop Charles Ferdinand of Breslau, the city of Breslau, the Dukes of Silesia-Liegnitz-Brieg, and for John George of Saxony.

126

George III Duke of Silesia, Liegnitz, and Brieg 1639-64

Oval silver medal, H. 39 mm., W. 37 mm.

D : G : GEORG : DUX SIL · L · & B : SUPREMAE · PER · SIL · PRAEF · ADMINISTR: Bust facing front, wearing wig, drapery over cuirass, with lion's head on right shoulder. Below: artist's signature I B, all within foliate frame.

Rev. · SORS · MEA · A · DOMINO Under three helmets and on baroque cartouche the quadripartite Liegnitz-Brieg shield.

Loebbecke Coll., Munich 1908, no. 713
Friedensburg und Seger, no. 1827
Forrer, I, 305/306

UNIDENTIFIED ARTIST, SEVENTEENTH CENTURY

127

Leopold I of Hapsburg 1640-1705, Emperor 1658-1705

Gold medal, H. 52 mm., W. 44 mm., no date (1658)

LEOPOLDVS. D G. ROM. IMPERATOR Laureate and armored bust to right, wearing sash of the Golden Fleece and drapery over shoulder.

Rev. CONSILIO · ET · INDVSTRIA The divine eye, over a crowned globe on which is a castle and a rock. To the sides, two arms extending from heaven holding sword and sceptre. Granulated field. Original suspension loop.

Joseph und Fellner, 1888

Commemorates the Emperor's coronation at Frankfurt.

Provenance: Dr. Paul Julius Coll.

JOHANN HOEHN Danzig c. 1637-93

The artist worked for the Danzig mint, the Electoral court of Brandenburg, and various other courts.

128

John Casimir King of Poland 1648-68

Silver medal, 69 mm. diam., 1658

IOANNES CASIMIRUS D. G. POLONIAE & SUECIAE REX etc. Laureate bust with long hair to right, wearing armor, drapery, and the sash of the Golden Fleece. Under the truncation, artist's signature: I H.

Rev. (rosette) NUMINIS AUSPICYS ET REGIS FORTIBUS ARMIS. THORUNIUM PRISCO REDDITUR OBSEQUIO. View of the city of Thorn, under the glorious name of God. In the foreground, encamped troops. Underneath, in a cartouche: M. D. C. LVIII. XXX DECEMBER.

Hutten-Czapski, no. 2109
Ossbahr, no. 22, pl. VII
Forrer, II, 522
Bahrfeldt, no. 9164
Raczinsky, no. 142
Vossberg, no. 358

Commemorates the capture of Thorn by John Casimir.

129

John Casimir

Silver medal, 43 mm. diam., 1660

IOAN · CASIM · D · G · REX · POL. & SUEC · M · D · L · R · PRUS · Laureate bust with long hair and moustache to right, wearing drapery over cuirass and the chain of the Golden Fleece. Under the truncation, artist's signature: · I. H.

Rev. PAX AETERNA AD GEDAN : A. CIƆIƆCLX · III · MAII · CONDITA. A crowned dove holding olive wreath over the city of Danzig. In the exergue, crowned olive and laurel wreaths, and signature: IH.

Hutten-Czapski, no. 2156
Frankiewicz Coll., no. 639

Commemorates the Peace of Oliva between Poland and Sweden.

130

John Hevelius Astronomer in Danzig 1611-87

Silver medal, 52 mm. diam., 1687

Draped half-bust with long hair facing front.

Rev. IOHANNES HEVELIUS | DANTISCAN CONSULVET CIVITAT. | DELICIUM REGUM AC PRINCIPUM | ASTRONOMORUM IPSE PRINCEPS | IN GLORIAM ATQUE ADMIRATIONEM | SECULI PATRIAE ORBIS | ANNO 1611 DIE 82 IANUARII NATUS | REM CONCILIIS PUBLICAM IUVIT | LITERARIAM PRAECELLENTIB. MONUMENT. | AUXIT | MERITIS IN UTRAMQUE ILLUSTRIS | SPLENDOREM NOMINIS AETERNITATI | INSERUIT | IPSO NATALI DIE | ANNO 1687 | DENATUS, and the artist's signature: I H.

Hutten-Czapski, no. 3899
Coll. in the Marienburg, no. 8852
Vossberg, no. 1105

Hevelius made valuable observations of the moon's surface, discovered four comets, and collected data for his catalogue of 1564 stars. He is most famous for his study of lunar topography, recorded in his *Selenographia* (1647), which is noted for excellent lunar maps.

PHILIPP HEINRICH MUELLER Augsburg 1654-1719

Mueller's parents being of modest means, he was obliged at a young age to begin providing for himself. A member of the Augsburg town council recognized the young man's artistic talents and took an interest in him. It was then Mueller learned medal engraving, an art in which he soon excelled.

Mueller's medals became known all over Europe, and many rulers and princes were portrayed by him. He was equally successful as a coin engraver. The dies for some of the most beautiful coins of the seventeenth century were cut by Mueller.

131

William III and Mary King and Queen of England 1688-94

Silver medal, 55 mm. diam., 1689

GVLIELMVS ET MARIA REX ET REGINA BRITANIAE. The two busts conjoined to right. Below, artist's signature: P. H. M.

Rev. AUREA FLORIGERIS SUCCRESCUNT POMA ROSETTIS. Liberty seated under orange tree from which the crown is suspended. She holds cap of liberty, scales of justice, and the cross. On exerguel line, artist's signature: P. H. M. Below the line: SECURITAS BRITANIAE RESTITUTA 1689.

Outer rim inscribed: EXTERNO MALE PRESSA IUGO BRITANNIA PRIDEM, IN PRISCAS ITERUM RESPIRAT LIBERA LEGES.

Franks and Grueber, no. 60
Van Loon, III, 412, no. 3
Forster, no. 657

Commemorates William and Mary's Coronation as King and Queen of England.

MARTIN HEINRICH OMEIS Nürnberg 1650-1703 Dresden

Omeis was employed at the Dresden mint as assistant engraver, with a yearly income of 124 gulden. Ernst Caspar Duerr taught him the art of die sinking. On several medals executed before 1680 we find their joint signatures.

132

John George III Elector of Saxony 1680-91

Silver medal, 33.5 mm. diam., 1691

· IOH · GEORG · III · D · SAX · I · C · M · A · & W · EL · Bust right, wearing wig, and ermine over plate armor with lion's head on shoulder. On the truncation, the artist's signature: O · f ·

Rev. COELITUS DATA in arch above; below, A TERRA DENEGATA · Divine hand issuing from the clouds, holding crown over globe. Outer rim inscribed: NAT · DRESDAE D 20 IUN · Aº 1647. DENAT · TUBINGAE Aº 1691 · D · 12 · SEPT ·

Tentzel, pl. LXIX, 8
Dassdorf Coll., no. 985

MARIA ANTONIO DI GENNARO also known as ANTONIO DE JANUARIO ac. Naples and Vienna d. 1744

A Neapolitan by birth, Di Gennaro worked for the King of Naples during his early career. By a resolution dated December 1713 he was appointed "Kaiserlicher Muenz-Eisenschneider" at the Vienna mint. To this period belongs the interesting medal on Count Waldstein who, as it would appear, took no minor pride in a prolific ancestor (cf. no. 133).

133

John Joseph Count of Waldstein

Silver medal, 72 mm. diam., 1716

The Count's ancestor, John Henry of Waldstein, offering in 1254 his twenty-four sons to King Primislav of Bohemia for participation in the King's crusade against the pagans.

The Count and his twenty-four sons arriving before the King. Above the exergue, the artist's signature: A · D · IANVARIO · F · ; in the field below: HEROICA FOECUNDITAS.

Rev. XXIV FILII | A PATRE IOAN:HENRICO | BARONE A WALDSTEIN | A:P:O:R:MCCLIIII | PRIMISLAO BOHEMIAE REGI | IN CRUCIATA CONTRA PRUTENOS | AD MILITIAM PRAESENTATI | FABIOS CCCVI TRANSGRESSI | QUI A VICTORES DE

HOSTE REDUCES | ET VITELLIIS SUPERIORES | NON IN UNA COLONIA | SED IN NUMEROSA PROSAPIA | SECULO NOSTRO DONATA | INDELEBILES

Outer rim inscribed: QUORUM MEMORIAM IOAN:IOS:COM:A WALDSTEIN. S:C: ET C:M:CAMER: HOC NUMO RESTITUIT 1716.

Forrer, II, 241
Brettauer, no. 4902
Donebauer Coll., no. 4026
Domanig, *Die Deutsche Medaille,* no. 735, pl. 83
Neumann, p. 668, 57; pl. LXXIV, 639

PETER PAUL WERNER Nürnberg 1689-1771

Werner worked for several German courts during his long period of activity which started about 1712 and lasted until his death.

PAUL GOTTLIEB NÜRNBERGER ac. 1709-46

Nürnberger was assistant mint-master of Nürnberg from 1709-21; thereafter, until his death in 1746, mint-master. In 1730 he went bankrupt, but was able to retain his office.

The following Prussian medal represents the combined effort of the two artists. The obverse is signed by Werner, the reverse by Nürnberger.

134

Frederick William I Elector of Brandenburg, King of Prussia 1713-40

Very large silver medal, 132.5 mm. diam., 1733

FRID · WILH · D · G · REX · BORVSS · EL · BRAND · Bust right, wearing wig, plate armor with aegis on breast, ermine, and sash. On the truncation, the artist's signature: P. P. Werner fec.

Rev. PRO DEO ET MILITE Under all-seeing eye, troops in parading formation. Underneath, on a ribbon: BEROL. M. DCCXXXIII. In the field, to the right, the artist's signature: N.

Ampach Coll., no. 11313
Henckel Coll., no. 1393

One of the largest struck medals. The obverse die for this medal burst while being tempered, and only three specimens are known to exist.

PAUL HEINRICH GOEDECKE ac. 1730-64

Goedecke, a Hamburg medallist, worked chiefly for the Danish court. He also executed several portrait medals of private persons. His medals are signed: P. H. G.

135

Frederick V 1723-66, King of Denmark and Norway 1746-66

Gold medal, 38 mm. diam., 1749

FRIED. V. DG. REX. DAN. NORV. VAN. GO. Youthful bust with wig right, wearing armor and drapery with ermine. On the truncation, the artist's signature: P. H. G.

Rev. HAC SECVLA IVBILANT VMBRA Under the raying sun, Dania as Minerva, seated on a throne adorned with the crowned royal cypher throwing its shadow over the 300-mark of a sundial. Dania holds the shields of the House of Oldenburg and of Denmark. In the exergue: OLDENB:DAN:TERTIA | VICE IVBILANS | D. 28. OCT. 1749.

Danske Mynter og Medailler, Suppl., pl. 3, no. 1
Galster, 418

Commemorates 300 years of rule by the House of Oldenburg.

FRANZ ANDREAS SCHEGA d. 1787

Schega was a self-taught medallist whose artistic ability has been much acclaimed. He filled the post of mint engraver and medallist at Munich beginning in 1738 and was appointed medallist to the court in 1751. The artist died blind.

136

Frederick Christian Crown Prince of Poland

Silver medal, 62 mm. diam., 1763

FRIDERIC · CHRIST · D · G · PR · REG · POL · & LITH · DUX SAX ·

& EL · Bust right, in elaborate baroque drapery. On the truncation, the artist's signature: F · A · SCHEGA · F ·

Rev. PIIS MANIBUS AUG · III · MAGNANIMI · Statue in mausoleum topped by rising eagle. In the exergue: OBIIT V · OCTOBRIS MDCC LXIII

Dassdorf, no. 1510
cf. Forrer, V, 377/8

BOHEMIAN MEDALS

CONCZ WELCZ ac. St. Joachimsthal c. 1527-53

There is little information about the origin of Welcz. The discovery, at the beginning of the sixteenth century, of the rich Bohemian silver mines (which gave their name to the "Erzgebirge," German for "Ore Mountain") may have contributed to the artist's ample medallic production. Especially popular with the local population were Biblical medals, often representing corresponding scenes from the Old and New Testaments. The style of Welcz and that of many of his Joachimsthal contemporaries are very similar, and it was not an uncommon practice among these artists to borrow or buy from one another their hubs and dies.

137

Resurrection | Prophet Jonas

Silver medal with old fire-gilding, 52 mm. diam., 1537

CHRVS · MORITVR · PRO · NOBIS · ET · RESVRGIT · VT · NOS IVSTOS · FACIAT · 46 · Christ rising from the tomb and holding a banner. Around the tomb, two warriors; to the right, a tree; in the left background, a tower. On the right wall of the tomb, the date 1537.

Rev. IANAS · QVI · POST · TRES · DIES · DE · PISTE · EXIVIT · DESIGNAT · CRISTI · RESSVREXIONEM · CAPITVLOZ · The bearded Prophet Jonas, his hands raised in prayer, emerging from the whale's mouth. In the left background, a castle and a ship.

Katz, no. 226

The obverse shows the influence of Moderno (cf. the plaquette, Molinier, I, 180). Katz believes the medal possibly to be from the workshop of the Leipzig Master, Hans Reinhart.

NICKEL MILICZ St. Joachimsthal ac. 1544-70

Etchings and woodcuts by artists like Hans Holbein, Hans Sebald Beham, Hirschvogel, and others often served as models for Milicz's medallic works. The first mention of the artist occurs in 1540 when he is named among the town councillors of Thal. During his artistic career, which stretched over twenty-five years, Milicz also cut dies for coins.

138

Charles V 1500-1558, Emperor 1519-56 and *Ferdinand I* 1503-64, King of Bohemia 1526-62 and Hungary 1526-63 (Emperor 1556-64)

Gilded silver medal, 60 mm. diam., 1550

PROGENIES DIVVM QVINTVS SIC CAROLVS ILLE IMPERII CAESAR LVMINA AET SVAE L Bareheaded and bearded bust right, wearing plate armor, with Golden Fleece on breast. Legend between double circles.

Rev. FERDINANDVS D G ROMANOR HVNGARI BOEMINI INFANS HISPA ARC AVS REX 1550 Bareheaded and bearded bust right, with long hair, wearing plate armor with Golden Fleece on breast. Legend between double circles.

Bernhart, *Die Bildnismedaillen Karls des Fünften,* no. 136, pl. XI
Herrgott, pl. IV, 39
Erbstein Coll., pl. I, 110
Lanna Coll., III, no. 649
Markl, no. 1984, pl. LIX
Montenuovo Coll., no. 605
Katz, no. 318, pl. XLV, 3

The portrait of Ferdinand is after a medal by Joachim Deschler, cf. Habich, *Corpus,* I, 2, no. 1616; pl. CLXXIV, 3

139

Maximilian II of Hapsburg 1527-76, Emperor 1564-76

Maximilian II, son of Ferdinand I and Anna, sister of Ludwig II of Hungary and Bohemia, was born 1527, elected King of Bohemia 1548, crowned 1562, King of the Romans from 1562, Emperor 1564, died 1576.

Silver medal, 53 mm. diam., 1566

MAXIMILIANVS · II · D · G · ROMA · IMPERI · SEM · AVG · GER · HV · BO · ETC · REX · Laureate and bearded bust right, wearing cuirass and chain with the Golden Fleece. Foliate border.

Rev. ARCHI · DVX · AVSTRI · DVX · BVRG · MARC · MOR · 1566 Double-headed imperial eagle under the crown of the Holy Roman Empire; in the center, the Hapsburg shield. Foliate border.

Katz, no. 326, pl. XLVI, 8
Domanig, *Die Deutsche Medaille*, no. 230
Katalog der Muenzen-und Medaillen-Stempel-Sammlung des K. K. Hauptmuenzamtes in Wien 1901, p. 45, no. 55; pl. XI, 1
Herrgott, pl. 8, 17
Provenance: Merzbacher Coll., Munich 1914, no. 86, pl. X

140

Creation of Eve | Marriage at Cana

Silver medal with old fire-gilding, 42 mm. diam., 1552

GOTT · LIES · ADAM · HART · ENTSCHLA · NAM · EIN · RIPP · A · S · S · M · D · D · EVA · G · Z · Adam in deep slumber below a tree, next to him God the Father raising Eve.

Rev. VFF · DER · HOCHZEIT · ZV · CANA · VERWANDELT · CHRISTVS · WASSE · Z · W IO · Z · The Marriage at Cana; below in a cartouche, 1552.

Katz, no. 370, pl. LVI
Loebbecke Coll., Munich 1908, no. 510
The Marriage at Cana is after an etching by Hans Sebald Beham. (G. Pauli, *Hans Sebald Beham,* Strassburg 1901, p. 36, no. 25)

UNIDENTIFIED ARTIST, SEVENTEENTH CENTURY

141

John Frederick of Waldstein Archbishop of Prague 1675-94

Gold medal, 33 mm. diam., 1688

IOANNES FRIDERIC ARCHIE · PRAG · Bust right, wearing ecclesiastical garb.

Rev. COMES DE WALDSTEIN Crowned coat of arms under archiepiscopal hat with infula. Underneath: 16*88

cf. Donebauer, 4633 (silver)
Commemorates the consecration of the Kreuzherrenkirche in Prague. Probably unique in gold.

MEDALS OF THE LOW COUNTRIES

JACOB JONGHELINCK Antwerp 1531-1606

Jonghelinck ranks as the most prolific Flemish medallist of his period and has a considerable repute as a sculptor as well. In 1558, while in the employ of Philip II, he executed the monument at Bruges to the memory of Charles the Bold, Duke of Burgundy.

In 1556, when only twenty-five years old, Jonghelinck engraved the seal of the Order of the Golden Fleece. In 1572 he became master of the mint at Antwerp. In addition to these assignments he also was active as a goldsmith and medallist; a document dated 1598 records a payment to him of 148 livres, 15 sous, and 9 deniers for four gold medals he had executed for Archduke Albert.

Jonghelinck during his early career was a pupil of Leone Leoni in Milan, which explains the Italian influence in his style. His medals are cast, sometimes subsequently chased, and without doubt the work of an accomplished artist.

142

Antoine Perrenot 1517-86, Cardinal Granvella

Silver medal, 58 mm. diam.

· ANTONII PERRENOT EPI · ATREBAT · Bareheaded and bearded bust right, wearing gown with high closed collar. Pearled border.

Rev. DVRATE Poseidon, in chariot drawn by sea horses, brandishing his trident and sinking Aeneas' ship. Beyond: a rainbow and two blowing zephyrs. Pearled border.

Armand, II, 255, 37
Plon, p. 275, pl. XXXIV, 3 (reverse)
Simonis, p. 109, pl. IX, 2
Bernhart, *Archiv.,* II, 3 (1920/21), no. 12, pl. VII
Provenance: Lanna Coll., III, no. 465, pl. 26
    Viscomte de Sartiges Coll.

UNIDENTIFIED ARTIST 1601

143

Nicholas van Delen Dutch patrician

Silver cachet, H. 28 mm., W. 41 mm., 1601

· B · NICOLAVS · VAN · DELEN · Under elaborately crested helmet, the coat of arms, two ram's heads on broad center bar. Dated: ANNO 1601.
The Van Delens were an old Dutch patrician family.

JURRIAAN POOL Amsterdam, mid-seventeenth century

Very little is known of the life of Pool. He may have been employed at the Utrecht mint as an engraver. Among his excellent medallic productions is the medal of Admiral Tromp, which bears his signature.

144

Admiral Martin Harpertszoon Tromp 1597-1653

Silver medal, 67 mm. diam., 1653

MARTEN · HARPERTS[!]EN · TROMP · RIDDER · Bareheaded bust facing front, wearing high-closed gown, and medallion on breast. Underneath: J. POOL.

Rev. LIEVTENANT · ADMIRAAL · VAN · HOLLAND · VOOR · HET · VAADERLAND · GESNEVVELT · DEN · 10 · AVGVSTI · ANNO 1653 · View of a naval battle, with two men-of-the-line in close action; in the foreground, sinking ship.

Van Loon, II, 364 (ill.)
Forrer, IV, 665, where this medal is quoted as "the most important of this artist's medals."

O. WOUTER MULLER ac. 1653-88

This Dutch artist of Amsterdam was one of the foremost masters of the repoussé medal. His medals are embossed, chased, and the two sides united by a rim. The Dutch legends possibly are composed by Muller himself; he injects into them his own name and states that they are the art of Muller.

145

Admiral Martin Harpertszoon Tromp

Silver repoussé medal, 70 mm. diam., 1653

Bust, three-quarters facing, in very high relief, surrounded by naval emblems, under crown held by two putti. Underneath, on a ribbon: "Mijn hert en hant was voor het lant."

Rev. (in italics): "Waarom doet Muller Tromp door kunst van gout en silver leeven : om dat hij d'ijzer eew door krijgsdeugd heeft verdreven." A naval engagement, with two men-of-war at close range in the foreground. At top: "den 10. Aug. 1653."

Franks and Grueber, p. 403, no. 34
Van Loon, II, 364, no. 3 (ill.)
Loebbecke Coll., Munich 1908, no. 195

Tromp's crushing of a Spanish fleet in the lee of the Downs in 1639 marked the passing of Spanish sea power in the seventeenth century.

146

Admiral Cornelis Evertsen d. 1666

Silver repoussé medal, 79 mm. diam., 1666

HEER EVERTS, MET TRIOMF, OP'T BED VAN EER GESNEEFT, ALDVS IN'T SILVER DOOR DE KUNST VAN MULLER LEEFT. Ao. 1666 den 11 Junii. Bust in high relief, three-quarters right, on naval trophies. On the truncation: CORN EVERTSEN-ADMIRAAL VAN ZEEL(and).

Rev. HIER STRYCKT HET BRITSCH GEWELT VOOR NEDERLANT DE VLAGH DE ZEE HEEFT NOIT GEWAEGHT VAN ZULT EEN ZWAEREN SLAGH. Sea battle between the Dutch and English fleets.

Van Loon, II, 529, 1
Forrer, IV, 195
Provenance: Viscomte de Sartiges Coll.

JAN FILIUS LUTMA Amsterdam c. 1605-85

Lutma's medals, though not numerous, are very fine in execution.

147

Joost van den Vondel 1587-1679, Dutch poet

Silver repoussé medal, 66 mm. diam., 1679

Draped bust facing front, within an olive wreath inscribed: JOOST VAN DEN VONDEL, gest. 5 Feb. 1679

Rev. Swan with open wings within an olive wreath inscribed: S'lants Outste en Grootste Poeet, geb. 17 Nov. 1587.

Van Loon, III, 283, 2
Koehler, XIV, 193
Forrer, III, 503

Van den Vondel wrote *Gysbreght van Aemstel* and other dramas, translated Tasso, Virgil, Ovid, Horace, Sophocles, and Euripides.

UNIDENTIFIED ARTISTS, SEVENTEENTH CENTURY

148

Nativity | Adoration of the Magi

Silver repoussé medal, 83 mm. diam.

The Virgin and St. Joseph kneeling on the ground, between them the

Child; on the right, two shepherds standing, the heads of the ox, the ass, and a tree; on the left, a shepherd carrying a crook; in the background, a building; above, the star of Bethlehem.

Rev. On the left, the Virgin seated holding the Child, behind her St. Joseph standing, before her the Three Kings, the foremost figure kneeling, and three children; on the right, the ox and the ass; in the background, a building; above, the star.

Apparently unpublished. Probably unique.

149

Anointing of Saul | Biblical Scene

Silver repoussé medal, 53 mm. diam.

Saul kneeling in front of Samuel. Saul in wide shepherd's garb, holding sceptre surmounted by a lily, receives the crown from bearded Samuel, who is wearing long gown and round cap. In the background, a city. Ornamental border.

Rev. Biblical scene.

Apparently unpublished.

150

Pope Adrian VI (Adriaen Floriszoon van Trusen of Utrecht 1459-1523) Pope 1522-23

Lead medal, 84.5 mm. diam.

P · M · ADRIAEN VAN GOD GHEKOREN PAVS VAN ROMEN T'UTRECHT GHEBOREN Bust left, wearing tiara and cope closed with a medallion. In the field, two coats of arms.

No reverse.

Van Mieris, II, 158, 3

cf. *Tresor, Med. des Papes,* p. 7, no. 6, note

ENGLISH, DANISH, AND SWEDISH MEDALS

BERNARD RANTWIC sixteenth century

Rantwic was of German origin but worked in London. Very few medals have been attributed to him.

151

Sir Richard Shelley b. 1514 Prior of England, Knight of Malta

Bronze medal, 71 mm. diam.

RICARDVS · SCELLEIVS PRIOR · ANGLIAE · Bearded half-bust right, wearing armor, the breastplate adorned with the Maltese cross. Under the truncation: BERN. RANTWIC. F.

Rev. PATRIARVM · EXVBITOR · OPVM A winged griffon, crowned, standing left in mountainous landscape.

Franks and Grueber, I, 127, 75

Forrer, V, 28

UNIDENTIFIED ENGLISH ARTIST, SIXTEENTH CENTURY

152

Elizabeth I 1533-1603, Queen of England 1558-1603

Oval silhouetted suspension medal of silver, H. 57.5 mm., W. 46.5 mm.

Bust left, with elaborately arranged hair, wearing ruff collar, richly brocaded dress with puffed sleeves and jewel. Broad foliate wreath.

Rev. Crowned royal cypher over Phoenix rising from the ashes (symbolizing the Queen's virginity). Broad foliate wreath.

An identical piece is in the British Museum.

ERICH PARISE Copenhagen, first half of the seventeenth century

153

Frederick III 1609-70, King of Denmark 1648-70 and his wife *Sophia Amalia of Brunswick*

Silver medal, 41 mm. diam., c. 1658

DOMINVS PROVIDEBIT King's bust to right, laureate, draped and armored. Under the truncation, in italics, the artist's signature: E P

Rev. SPES MEA IN DEO Queen's bust left, draped. Under the truncation, in italics: E P

Danske Mynter og Medailler, pl. XVIII, 4, var.

Galster, no. 81

J. HERCLAS Copenhagen, ac. mid-seventeenth century

154

The Relief of Copenhagen by a Dutch Fleet after the Naval Victory of Cronenborg

Silver medal, 46.5 mm. diam., 1658

View of the city and harbor of Copenhagen with ships at anchor. Above, on a ribbon: HAFNIA DANIAE.

Rev. Naval battle. Three ships-of-the-line, flying the Dutch, Swedish, and United Provinces flags, in close combat; a sinking ship in the foreground. In the right background: Kronborg Castle. On a floating piece of wreckage, the artist's initials: I H

Danske Mynter og Medailler, pl. XX, no. 2

Van Loon, II, 430, 2 (ill.)

Ossbahr, p. 87, no. 21, pl. VI

After Copenhagen had been besieged for two months by the land and naval forces of Charles X Gustav of Sweden, a Dutch fleet of thirty-five ships, mounting 1170 guns, under the command of Baron Opdam van Wassenaer, arrived on October 23, 1658. Following a fierce engagement with the Swedish fleet and heavy losses on both sides, the Dutch forced their way into the port of Copenhagen and landed food supplies and troops.

K. RULL Sweden, first half of the seventeenth century

155

Gustav II Adolf 1594-1632, King of Sweden 1611-32

Silver medal, 28 mm. diam., 1632

GUST · ADOL · D : G · SUEC · GOT · VAND · REX · M · PRIN · FIN · DV · ETH · ET CAR · IG D · Within a quadrilobe, laureate and bearded bust right, and the legend: NAT 9 DEC: 1594 DENAT · 6 NOV: 1632

Rev. · STANS ACIE · PVGNANS · VINCENS · MORIENSQ · TRIVMPHAT · Crowned sword, laurel and palm branch tied together. In the background, a landscape with river and sailboat.

Hildebrand, I, no. 179

Crona Coll., no. 116

Forrer, V, 268

Commemorates the King's death in the Battle of Luetzen.

ITALIAN PLAQUETTES ATTRIBUTED TO ARTISTS

AGOSTINO DI DUCCIO Florence 1418-98

This great Italian master worked during the middle of the Quattrocento. Only two plaquettes have been ascribed to him. Eric MacLagan (*Burlington Magazine* 1920, pp. 166 ff.) writes: "Agostino (di Duccio) sculpture is extremely rare."

Little is known about Duccio's life; he was active at Modena, Venice, Rimini, and Perugia. In 1446 he was banished from Florence.

156

Pietà

Rectangular bronze plaquette, H. 128 mm., W. 198 mm.

In the center, the veiled Virgin, across her knees the Body of Christ, supported by grief-stricken female figures. To the right, Joseph of Arimathea carries the crown of thorns. To the left, Nicomedes holds the nails of the cross.

Molinier, no. 83 (the Louvre specimen, formerly in the His de la Salle Coll.)

Provenance: Count Trivulzio Coll.

PIERO JACOPO DI ANTONIO ALARI BUONACOLSI called L'ANTICO c. 1460-1528

The places of L'Antico's principal activity were Mantua, Bozzolo, and Gazzuolo, where he was employed by Federigo and Gianfrancesco Gonzaga. Many of his works are inspired by classical subjects, which explains his nickname.

157

Roman Empress Faustina c. 125-176

Circular bronze plaquette, 39 mm. diam.

DIVA FAVSTINA Bust facing front, her head slightly inclined to left, two strands of hair falling over her shoulders, wearing softly draped gown. Two incised border lines. High relief.

Rev. SENATS POPLS A triumphal procession, marching towards the right, a warrior bearing a shield, two horsemen, a standard bearer, a trophy bearer, and a nude captive, his head turned backwards. In the exergue, various weapons and pieces of armor. On an oval shield, the letter M.

cf. Molinier, no. 516 (obverse), no. 640 (reverse)
cf. De Ricci, *Dreyfus Coll.*, no. 121 (reverse)
cf. Victoria and Albert Museum, no. 86 (reverse)

cf. Bange, *Reliefs und Plaketten*, nos. 491 and 492 (reverse)
cf. Migeon, *Les Arts*, no. 80 (August 1908), p. 22, 10 (reverse)

ANDREA BRIOSCO called IL RICCIO (the curly-haired) 1470-1532

Among the sons of Padua, Riccio's name holds an honored place. As an architect he built the Church of Santa Giustina at Padua, as a bronze worker he created some unrivalled objects of decorative art, but his masterpiece is the bronze candelabra in Sant'Antonio at Padua, the most beautiful of its kind in the world.

158

Judith

Rectangular bronze plaquette, H. 108 mm., W. 83 mm.

Judith is standing in front view, bending towards the right, about to drop into a bag, held open with both hands by an old woman, also in front view, the head of Holofernes, which she holds by the hair in her right hand. Raised base line. High relief.

Molinier, no. 218
British Museum (T. W. Greene specimen), no. 97
Migeon, no. 321 (Louvre specimen)
Musée Jacquemart-André, no. 493
Paris, *Cabinet des Medailles* (Armand-Valton bequest no. 2529)
Bange, *Die Italienischen Bronzen*, no. 356
Florence (Carrand Coll.), no. 400
De Ricci, *Dreyfus Coll.*, no. 125
Migeon, *Les Arts,* no. 80 (August 1908), p. 25
Detroit Institute of Arts, *Decorative Arts of the Italian Renaissance 1400-1600*, no. 325 (this specimen)
Bode, *Die Italienischen Bronzen*, 1904

After a composition by Mantegna, engraved by Girolamo Mocetto (B. 1).
cf. Planiscig, *Riccio*, p. 436.

 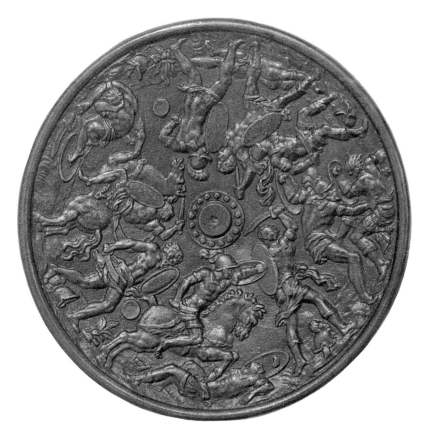

MODERNO

According to Molinier, "Moderno" was only a cognomen, and he identifies the artist as Vettor di Antonio Gambello, called "Camelio," a Venetian, to whose works Moderno's creations bear great similarity.

In a treatise by Francis Holland (1549), Moderno is mentioned as an engraver of leaden seals (papal bullae), which would indicate that the artist also worked in Rome. Camelio was superintendent of the Papal mint under Leo X, about 1515.

159

Crucifixion

Rectangular silver plaquette (bronze frame), H. 235 mm., W. 128 mm.

On a tall cross, Christ between the two thieves. At the foot of the cross, on the left, the Virgin fainting in the arms of two women; near them, a nude child. Behind them, St. John standing with clasped hands, and the Magdalene embracing the cross. Around them, a number of soldiers on horseback and on foot, a horseman on the right wielding his club at one of the thieves. The soldiers armed with halberds and shields.

The plaquette is set in a rectangular frame with rounded top. On the side columns, ecclesiastical designs; at the bottom, on each side, three mourning angels; in the center, floral garland and two putti. The top border bears five medallions, the center one depicting the Dove. In the upper half-round field, in very high relief, God the Father facing front, blessing.

De Ricci, *Dreyfus Coll.,* no. 170
Molinier, no. 171
British Museum, no. 38
Bange, *Reliefs und Plaketten,* no. 454
Migeon, *Les Arts,* no. 80 (August 1908), p. 20, vi
Florence (Carrand Coll.), nos. 47 and 48
Oxford (Ashmolean Museum), nos. 58 and 59
Louvre, no. 301 (gift of Gustave Dreyfus, 1875)
Paris, *Cabinet des Medailles* (Armand-Valton), nos. 2510 and 2539
Detroit Institute of Arts, *Decorative Arts of the Italian Renaissance 1400-1600,* no. 329A, ill. p. 141 (this specimen)
Provenance: Count Trivulzio Coll.

160

Crucifixion

Rectangular bronze plaquette, H. 125 mm., W. 88 mm.
As before, but with different detail and without frame.
Provenance: Gutekunst Coll., 20, 330, pl. x

161

Roman Combat

Circular concave bronze plaquette (perhaps the decorative bottom of a bowl), 110 mm. diam.

Around an ornamented circular shield, many-figured battle scene between horsemen and foot soldiers, some cuirassed and helmeted. Raised border.

Apparently unpublished and unique.

For style, cf. De Ricci, *Dreyfus Coll.,* nos. 216 and 217
Provenance: Luccardi Coll.

MASTER IO. F. F. North Italian c. 1500

162

Judgement of Paris

Circular bronze plaquette with traces of gilding, 56.7 mm. diam.

Paris seated left on a rock under a tree, presenting the apple to Venus who extends her right hand to receive it. Behind her Juno and Minerva standing, the latter holding a dagger (?), a spear, and a shield. Above, Cupid flying. Plain linear border.

Molinier, no. 134
Bange, *Reliefs und Plaketten,* no. 652
Molthein Coll., no. 55

JACOPO SANSOVINO, SCHOOL OF, SIXTEENTH CENTURY

163

Coronation of the Virgin

Rectangular bronze plaquette, H. 133 mm., W. 87 mm.

Christ, enthroned on clouds, lowering the crown on the head of the kneeling Mary, veiled, and surrounded by nine winged putti.

Molinier, no. 509
Bode, *Die Italienischen Bronzen,* no. 1273
Braun, p. 406
Bange, *Die Bildwerke des Deutschen Museums,* no. 944
Forrer, V, p. 332
Loebbecke Coll., Munich 1908, n. 836, pl. xxxx
Molthein Coll., no. 90, pl. 4

159

163

GIOVANNI BERNARDI DA CASTELBOLOGNESE 1496-c. 1555

Bernardi is known not only for the production of medals and plaquettes, which frequently depict classical scenes, but also for his success as an engraver of crystal and other precious stones. His most celebrated work in this field is the Farnese Casket in the Naples Museum.

On the occasion of Charles V's coronation at Bologna in 1530 as King of Lombardi, Bernardi cut the dies for a medal which so pleased the Emperor that he not only paid him 100 pistoles but also invited him to Spain. Bernardi, however, preferred to return to Rome, where most of his work was executed.

164

Roman Combat (Battle at Cannae?)

Circular convex silver badge, 41.4 mm. diam.

A fierce battle scene between mounted troops, helmeted and cuirassed and armed with spears and swords.

Apparently unpublished and unique.

GIAN FEDERIGO BONZAGNA called FEDERIGO PARMENSE ac. 1547-75

165

Adoration of the Shepherds

Rectangular bronze plaquette, H. 198 mm., W. 148 mm., 1561

In a basket placed on a broken column, the Christ Child, surrounded by Mary, Joseph, John, and the shepherds offering a lamb. To the right, the heads of the ox and the ass. In the background, an arch carried by columns, its frieze inscribed · PARM · INVENT · On the broken column in front, the date 1561. Beyond the arch, a round tower and a tall building. To the left in the sky, the star. Raised border.

cf. Bange, *Die Bildwerke des Deutschen Museums,* no. 42
Braun, p. 406
Faure Coll., no. 665, pl. xxiv
Molthein Coll., no. 64, pl. 8

166

Entombment

Rectangular bronze plaquette, H. 248 mm., W. 195 mm.

Two bearded men lowering the partly draped body of Christ into the tomb, behind which Mary, the Magdalene, and two other female figures stand, veiled and in an attitude of grief. To the right, the bareheaded St. John. In the background, an arch partly overgrown with shrubbery and grass.

Apparently unpublished and unique.

Provenance: Dr. Benno Geiger Coll.

ITALIAN PLAQUETTES BY UNIDENTIFIED ARTISTS

FLORENTINE, FIFTEENTH CENTURY

167

Emperor Augustus 31 B.C.-A.D. 14

Oval bronze plaquette, H. 50 mm., W. 34 mm.

Bust of the youthful Augustus to left, laureate, wearing cuirass and mantle; on breast, aegis.

cf. De Ricci, *Dreyfus Coll.,* no. 53, pl. xviii
cf. Bange, *Reliefs und Plaketten,* no. 202
cf. Oxford (Ashmolean Museum), nos. 17 and 18

ROMAN, FIFTEENTH CENTURY

168

Sixtus IV (Francesco della Rovere 1414-84), Pope 1471-84

Lead papal bolla, 37 mm. diam.

(crosslet) | SIXTVS | · PAPA · | · IIII · Pearled border.

Rev. PP | AE In high relief, the three-quarters facing heads of St. Peter and St. Paul, haloed. Between them, a tall cross rising from orb.

This bolla still retains the cord with which it was attached to a papal document.

VENETIAN, SIXTEENTH CENTURY

169

Andrea Gritti Doge of Venice 1523-39

Gold ducal bolla (sigillum), 36 mm. diam.

AND · GRITI · S(anctus) M(arcus) · VENET(iarum) · DVX Andrea Gritti standing, wearing wide gown and ducal hat, receiving the banner from haloed St. Mark, who holds the Bible.

No reverse.

British Museum, *Catalogue of Seals,* vi, 373, nos. 22, 222 (sulphur cast)
Detroit Institute of Arts, *Decorative Arts of the Italian Renaissance 1400-1600,* p. 100 (text and illustration) and p. 132, no. 317 (this specimen)
Probably unique.

Provenance: said to have been in the possession of the Ruzzini family of Venice.

165

Bolle (seals) were attached to documents, much as seals are today. Mostly they are of lead, in rare cases of silver, in bearing with the importance of the document or treaty to which they were attached. Golden bulls (bolla d'oro or sigillum aureum) are great rarities, since they were used only in exceptional cases. Very few have come down to us.

170
Christ Carrying the Cross
Rectangular bronze plaquette, H. 124 mm., W. 88 mm.
Surrounded by mercenaries and henchmen, Christ carries the cross, followed by two holy women. To the left, the kneeling St. Veronica with veil in her hands. In the background, a city wall.
Apparently unpublished. Probably unique. A great masterpiece by an unidentified artist.
Provenance: Count Trivulzio Coll.

171
Entombment
Rectangular bronze plaquette, H. 96 mm., W. 70 mm.
In a rocky landscape, the body of the Savior being lowered into the tomb; behind, Mary and another woman, veiled, in an attitude of grief; to the right, the kneeling Magdalene kissing the Savior's hand. In the background, Golgotha under the rising moon; in the foreground, a water bowl and an ointment vessel.
Provenance: Imbert Coll.

172
Ornamental Plaquette
Mandorla-shaped bronze plaquette, H. 174 mm., W. 57 mm.
Probably made to be affixed to a piece of furniture. In the center, a lion rampant to the left, surrounded by elaborate scrollwork, in silhouette.
No other specimen of this ornamental appliqué seems to be recorded. Probably unique.

NORTH ITALIAN, MID-SIXTEENTH CENTURY

173
Entombment
Shield-shaped bronze plaquette with old fire-gilding, H. 188 mm., W. 140 mm.
The body of Christ, supported by Mary and John, at the rocky entrance of the cave. Mary is veiled, St. John with flowing hair wears shepherd's garb. Underneath, broad border with three angels' heads and two palmettos.
Provenance: Molthein Coll., no. 108, pl. 7

174
Head of Christ
Oval bronze plaquette, H. 48 mm., W. 34 mm.
Head of Christ wearing the crown of thorns. Within elaborate Renaissance frame with foliate motifs.
cf. Bange, *Reliefs und Plaketten,* no. 926

175
Head of Christ
Square bronze plaquette, H. 46.5 mm., W. 36 mm.
Head of Christ to left.
Gallerie Nazionali Italiane, IV, 248

ITALIAN, SIXTEENTH CENTURY

176
Emperor Tiberius A.D. 14-37
Circular bronze plaquette, 85 mm. diam.
TIBER · CAESAR · Laureate bust right, with hair to nape of neck. Raised border.
Planiscig, I, 172, 330

177
Emperor Caligula A.D. 37-41
Oval bronze plaquette, H. 106.5 mm., W. 85 mm.
Laureate bust right, underneath: C · CAES · T · D All within a broad border of Roman armaments, interrupted by four lions' facing front.

178
Emperor Vespasian A.D. 69-79
Circular bronze plaquette, 86 mm. diam.
VESPASIAN · AVG · C · Laureate bust right, with hair to nape of neck. Raised border.
Planiscig, I, 172, 330

179
Emperor Trajan A.D. 98-117
Oval bronze plaquette, H. 56.5 mm., W. 44 mm.
Laureate bust right, hair to nape of neck, on granulated field. Very high relief.
Unpublished and probably unique.

173

183

FRENCH AND FLEMISH PLAQUETTES

UNIDENTIFIED ARTISTS

FRENCH, EARLY SIXTEENTH CENTURY

180

Francis I 1494-1547, King of France 1515-47

Bronze plaquette, H. 150 mm., W. 98 mm., c. 1535

The King's bearded portrait to right, wearing cap with broad brim, fur-collared coat over pleated robe, and necklace with pendant. All within double-lined raised border and cartouche of elaborate scrollwork; to the sides two fish-tailed mermaids supporting the upper part of the frame with the French fleur-de-lis in center. At the bottom, floral ornaments with antique mask in the center.

Apparently unpublished and unique.

Provenance: Count Trivulzio Coll.

FRENCH, SIXTEENTH CENTURY

181

Henry IV 1553-1610, King of France 1598-1610

Oval bronze plaquette, H. 59 mm., W. 47 mm.

Half-bust left, bearded and with long hair, wearing ruff collar, sash with cross over striped gown. Granulated field.

Apparently unpublished.

FLEMISH, SIXTEENTH CENTURY

182

The Triumph of Wisdom

Rectangular bronze plaquette, H. 63 mm., W. 124 mm.

On a four-wheeled chariot, driven by an old man and drawn by two unicorns, are seated four female figures. One bearing a yoke, the second holding a sceptre (and perhaps a bird), the third with crossed hands, the fourth (Wisdom) holding a bunch of keys; above her head, the Holy Ghost. Raised base line.

De Ricci, *Dreyfus Coll.*, no. 428, pl. cxx
Molinier, no. 665
Paris, *Cabinet des Medailles*, no. 2474
Bange, *Die Bildwerke des Deutschen Museums*, II, 133, no. 1490
Vienna, *Estensische Kunstsammlung*, no. 458
Padua, Rizzoli, no. 78

Exhibited: Detroit Institute of Arts, "Flanders in the Fifteenth Century," October-December, 1960

GERMAN PLAQUETTES

UNIDENTIFIED ARTIST, NÜRNBERG(?), SIXTEENTH CENTURY

183

Christ Carrying the Cross

Bronze plaquette with old fire-gilding, H. 161 mm., W. 123 mm.

On stony ground with a serpent and a tree stump in the foreground, Christ carrying the Cross. Behind him to left, veiled Mary and St. John standing.

Upper part silhouetted.

Middeldorf and Goetz, *Morgenroth Coll.*, no. 381 as unique

Second specimen known.

Provenance: Commerzienrat Bauer Coll.

184

186

GERMAN, SIXTEENTH CENTURY (after ALBRECHT DÜRER)

184

Entombment

Rectangular bronze plaquette, H. 129 mm., W. 97 mm.

Three men lowering the body of Christ into the tomb. To the left, the kneeling Magdalene placing the ointment vessel on the edge of the grave; behind her, a second kneeling woman and Mary and John standing. In the background, to the right, a grotto; to the left, a city.

After the *Entombment* by Albrecht Dürer, cf. *Kleine Passion.*

Willi Kurth, *Albrecht Dürer, sämtliche Holzschnitte,* München 1927, no. 250 (from the *Kleine Passion* 1511, entitled: Passio Christi ab Alberto Dürer Nurenbergensi, effigiata cum variis carminibus Fratris Benedicti Chelidonii Musophili, Nurenberg 1511).

Provenance: Gutekunst Coll., no. 374
    Viscomte de Sartiges Coll.

SOUTH GERMAN, END OF THE SIXTEENTH CENTURY

185

Flight into Egypt

Rectangular bronze plaquette with old fire-gilding, H. 169 mm., W. 126 mm.

Mary, the Child in her arm, seated on a donkey which, together with an ox, is led by Joseph, who turns his head towards Mary and points the way with his hand. To the left, dense woods; to the right, some trees.

Stony ground with grass and flowers in the foreground. In the background, a village. On the upper left, emerging from the clouds, are seven angels looking down at the Holy Family.

Apparently unpublished and unique.

In the style of Albrecht Altdorfer (1488-1538). cf. Baldass 1941, p. 297, *Farewell of the Disciples,* and landscapes, pp. 300-301.

Provenance: Commerzienrat Bauer Coll.

SPANISH PLAQUETTES

UNIDENTIFIED ARTISTS c. 1600

186

St. Francis

Rectangular bronze plaquette with traces of old silver, H. 122 mm., W. 90 mm.

Before the crucifix, St. Francis, haloed, his head turned upward in ecstasy, his hands with the stigmatas raised in prayer. In the background, rocky landscape. At the foot of the crucifix, a skull.

187

St. Peter

Rectangular bronze plaquette in wooden frame with gilded scrollwork and angel's head on top, H. 197 mm., W. 148 mm.

Half-bust of St. Peter under a tree, his hands clasped in prayer, looking towards heaven; in front of him, the keys. To the left, a column on which the cock is crowing.

Braun, *Archiv,* III (1921/22), 15 ff.
Imbert Coll., no. 215
Loebbecke Coll., Munich 1908, no. 854

185

LITERATURE TO WHICH REFERENCE IS MADE

Archiv für Medaillen- und Plakettenkunde Halle 1913-26. Quoted as *Archiv*

Archivio Storico dell'Arte 1888-97

Arethuse *Monnaies et Medailles. Sceaux. Gemmes* 1925-31

Armand, A. *Les Medailleurs Italiens des quinzieme et seizieme Siecles* Paris 1883-87

Babelon, J. *Great Coins and Medals* London 1959

Bahrfeldt, E. *Die Münzen- und Medaillen-Sammlung der Marienburg* Danzig 1900-16

Baldass, L. von in *Jahrbuch der kunsthistorischen Sammlungen des allerhöchsten Kaiserhauses* Vienna

Bange, F. R. *Die Italienischen Bronzen der Renaissance und des Barock* Berlin 1904

—— *Reliefs und Plaketten* Berlin 1922

Berlin *Amtliche Berichte aus den Königlichen Kunstsammlungen* by J. Menadier 1880-

—— *Königliche Museen zu. Sammlung von Renaissance-Kunstwerken gestiftet von Herrn James Simon zum 18. Oktober 1904* Berlin 1908. Quoted as *Simon*

Berliner Münzblätter by E. Bahrfeldt Berlin 1902-26

Bern Kunstmuseum Special catalogue *Kunst und Kunstgewerbe* Bern 1939-40

Bernhart, M. *Die Bildnismedaillen Karls des Fünften* Munich 1919

—— *Medaillen und Plaketten* Berlin 1911

Betts, C. W. *American Colonial History illustrated by Contemporary Medals* New York 1894

Binder, C. *Württembergische Münz- und Medaillenkunde* Stuttgart 1846

Bode, W. von *Florentiner Bildhauer der Renaissance* Berlin 1911

—— *Die Italienischen Bronzen* Berlin 1904

—— *Jahrbuch der Preussischen Kunstsammlungen* Berlin

—— *Zeitschrift für Bildende Kunst* XV (1904)

Bolzenthal, H. *Kunstgeschichte der modernen Medaillen-Arbeit* Berlin 1840

Bonanni, F. *Numismata Pontificum Romanorum* Rome 1699

Braun, E. W. *Kunst und Kunsthandwerk* 1917

Brettauer, J. *Medicina in Nummis.* Vienna 1937

British Museum *Catalogue of Seals in the Department of Manuscripts* London 1887-1900

—— *Coins of the Roman Empire* London 1923-62

—— C. F. Keary *Guide to the Exhibition of Italian Medals* London 1893 Quoted as *Keary*

—— G. F. Hill *Guide to the Exhibition of Medals of the Renaissance* London 1923

—— *Select Italian Medals of the Renaissance* London 1920

Burlington Magazine London 1903-

Calabi, A. and Cornaggia, G. *Matteo de' Pasti* 1926

Calvo y del Rivero *Guia del Salon de Numismatica* Museo Arqueologico Nacional Madrid 1926

Cecchi, G. B. *Monumenta ad Alam.Rinucc.* Florence 1791

Cicognara, L. *Storia della Scultura* Prato 1823-24

Cohen, H. *Description Historique des Monnaies frappées sous l'Empire Romain* Paris 1880-92

Corpus Nummorum Italicorum Rome 1910-40

Danske Mynter og Medailler Copenhagen 1791

Dassdorf, K. W. *Numismatisch-historischer Leitfaden zur Übersicht der Sächsischen Geschichte* Dresden 1801

De Bildt *Les Medailles Romaines de Christine de Suede* Rome 1908

Demiani, H. *Francois Briot, Caspar Enderlein and the Tin* Leipzig 1897

De Ricci, S. *The Gustave Dreyfus Collection. Reliefs and Plaquettes* Oxford 1931

Detroit Institute of Arts *Decorative Arts of the Italian Renaissance 1400-1600* Detroit 1958-59

—— *Flanders in the Fifteenth Century* Detroit 1960

Domanig, K. *Die Deutsche Medaille* Vienna 1907

—— *Porträtmedaillen des Erzhauses Österreich* Vienna 1896

Erman, A. *Die Deutschen Medailleure des 16. und 17. Jahrhunderts* Berlin 1885

Exter, F. *Versuch einer Sammlung von Pfältzischen Medaillen, Schau- und Gedächtnis- und allerley anderen Müntzen* Zweybrücken 1759-75

Fabriczy, C. von *Italian Medals* London 1904

Forrer, L. *Bibliographical Dictionary of Medallists* London 1904-30

Forster, A. von *Die Münzen und Medaillen von Augsburg* Leipzig 1910-14

Foville, J. de *Bulletin de l'Art ancienne et moderne* February 15, 1914

Frankfurter Münzzeitung

Franks, A. W. and Grueber, H. A. *Medallic Illustrations of British History* London 1885

Friedensburg and Seger *Schlesiens Münzen und Medaillen der neueren Zeit* Breslau 1901

Friedlaender, J. *Die Italienischen Schaumünzen des Fünfzehnten Jahrhunderts* Berlin 1882

Gallerie Nazionali Italiane Rome 1894-99

Galster, G. *Danske og Norske Medailler og Jetons ca. 1533-ca. 1788* Copenhagen 1936

Gazette des Beaux-Arts 1859-1903

Giovio, P. *Dialogo dell'Imprese* Lyon 1574

Gruyer, G. *L'Art Ferrarais* Paris 1897

Habich, G. *Die Deutschen Schaumünzen des XVI. Jahrhunderts* Munich 1929-34. Quoted as Habich *Corpus*

────── *Jahrbuch der Preussischen Kunstsammlungen* Berlin

────── *Die Medaillen der Italienischen Renaissance* Stuttgart and Berlin 1924

Hauschild's Beitrag zur neueren Münz- und Medaillengeschichte Dresden 1805

Heiss, A. *Les Medailleurs de la Renaissance* Paris 1881-92

Heraeus, C. G. *Bildnisse der regierenden Fürsten und berühmter Männer* Vienna 1828

Herrera, A. *Revista de Arqueologia*

Herrgott, M. *Nummotheca Principum Austriae* Freiburg 1752-53

Hildebrand, B. E. *Sveriges och Svenska Konungahusets Minnespenningar* Stockholm 1874-75

Hill, G. F. *A Corpus of Italian Medals of the Renaissance before Cellini* London 1930

────── *The Gustave Dreyfus Collection Renaissance Medals* Oxford 1931

────── *Medals of the Renaissance* Oxford 1920

────── *Pisanello* London 1905

────── *Portrait Medals of Italian Artists of the Renaissance* London 1912. Quoted as *Hill PMIA*

Hind, A. M. *Catalogue of early Italian Engravings* London 1930

Holbrook, R. T. *Portraits of Dante from Giotto to Raffael* London 1911

Hutten-Czapski, E. *Catalogue des Medailles et Monnaies Polonaises* St. Petersburg and Paris 1871-1916

Imbert, E. *Le Placchette Italiane della Raccolta* (by G. Morazzoni) Milan 1941

Imhof, C. A. *Nürnbergisches Münzkabinett* Nürnberg 1780-82

Jahrbuch der Kunsthistorischen Sammlungen des Allerhöchsten Kaiserhauses Vienna

Joseph, P. and Fellner, E. *Die Münzen von Frankfurt am Main* Frankfurt 1896

Juncker, C. *Das Guldene und Silberne Ehren-Gedächtniss D. Martini Lutheri* Frankfurt and Leipzig 1706

Katz, V. *Die Erzgebirgische Prägemedaille des XVI. Jahrhunderts* Prague 1932

Keary see British Museum

Koehler, J. D. *Historische Münzbelustigungen* Nürnberg 1729-65

Kurth, W. *Albrecht Dürer, sämtliche Holzschnitte* München 1927

Lancetti, V. *Memorie intorno ai Poeti laureati d'ogni tempo e d'ogni nazione* Milan 1839

Lawrence, R. H. *The Paduans Medals by Giovanni Cabino* 1964

Litta, P. *Famiglie Celebri Italiane* Milan 1819-85

Loehr, A. *Sammlung Erzherzog Franz Ferdinand* Vienna

Luccardi, C. *La Raccolta Luccardi a Milano* Milan

Markl, M. *Die Münzen und Medaillen Ferdinand I* Prague 1896

Martinori, E. *Annali della Zecca di Roma* Rome 1917

Mazerole, F. *Les Medailleurs français du XVe Siecle au Milieu du XVIIe* Paris 1902-04

Mazzuchellianum Museum, seu Numismata . . . Venice 1761-63. Quoted as *Mazzuchelli*

Menadier, J. *Schaumünzen des Hauses Hohenzollern* Berlin 1901

Metzler, W. P. *Die Medaillen und Plaketten der Kunstsammlung* (by J. Cahn) Frankfurt 1898

Middeldorf, U. and Goetz, O. *Medals and Plaquettes from the Sigmund Morgenroth Collection* Chicago 1953

Migeon, G. *Les Arts* Paris 1907-08

Molinier, E. *Les Plaquettes* Paris 1886

Morazzoni see Imbert

Morgenroth see Middeldorf

Nanni, A. *Medaglioni Estensi*

Naples. De Rinaldis *Medaglie dei Secoli XV e XVI nel Museo Nazionale di Napoli* Naples 1913

Neumann, J. *Böhmische Privatmünzen* Prague 1852-70

Numismatic Chronicle London

Oldenburg, J. F. H. *Samling af Svenska, Svenska Besittningarnas och Landgreven Fredriks Hessiska Mynt* Stockholm 1883

Ossbahr, C. A. *Mynt och Medaljer slagna for fraemmande Makter i Anledning av Krig mot Sverige* Uppsala 1927

Otrange-Mastai, M. L. d' "A Collection of Renaissance Jewels in the Possession of Martin J. Desmoni" *The Connoisseur* April 1957

Paris. Cabinet des Medailles Jean Babelon Bibliotheque Nationale

Paris. Louvre *Catalogue des Bronzes* Paris 1904

Passerini, G. L. *Il Ritratto di Dante* 1921

Pauli, G. *Hans Sebald Beham* Strassburg 1901

Planiscig, L. *Kunsthistorische Museen in Wien. Die Bronzeplastiken* Vienna 1924

Plon, E. *Leone Leoni et Pompeo Leoni* Paris 1887

Raczynski, E. *Le Medaillier de Pologne* Berlin-Breslau 1838-45

Regling, K. *Berichte der Preussischen Kunstsamm-lungen XLI* Berlin 1920

Revue Numismatique Blois and Paris 1836-

Rizzini, P. *Illustrazione dei Civici Musei di Brescia* Brescia 1892

Rodocanachi, E. P. *La Femme Italienne avant, pen-dant et apres la Renaissance* Paris 1922

Rondot, N. *Les Medailleurs et les Graveurs de Mon-naies ... en France* Paris 1904

Roville, G. *Prontuario delle Medaglie* Lyon 1553

Saglio, E. *L'Art* Paris 1893

Sallet, F. von *Untersuchungen über Albrecht Dürer* Berlin 1874

Simon see Berlin

Simonis, J. *L'Art du Medailleur en Belgique* Brussels and Jemeppe-sur-Meuse 1900-04

Spiess, J. J. *Brandenburgische historische Münzbe-lustigungen* Ansbach 1768-74

Streber, F. J. *Erinnerung an Pfalzgraf Karl. (Vortrag der Koeniglichen Akademie der Wissenschaften)* Munich 1812

Supino, I. B. *Il Medagliere Mediceo nel Reale Museo Nazionale di Firenze* Florence 1899

Tentzel, W. E. *Saxonia Numismatica* Dresden 1705-14

Thurston, H. *Holy Year of Jubilee* Westminster, Maryland 1900

Tormo. *Boletin de la Sociedad Espanola*

Tourneur in Kervijn de Lettenhove. Toison d'Or 1908

Trapesnikoff, T. *Die Porträtdarstellungen der Medi-ceer des XV. Jahrhunderts* Strassburg 1909

Tresor de Numismatique et de Glyptique Paris 1834-36

Van Loon, G. *Histoire Metallique des 17 Provinces des Pays-Bas* The Hague 1732-37

Van Mieris, F. *Histori der Nederlandsche Vorsten* The Hague 1732

Venice. Museo Civico Correr *Catalogo delle Monete, Medaglie, Tessere, Bolle e Placchette* Venice 1898

Venturi, A. *Storia dell'Arte Italiana* Milan 1901-39

Venuti, R. *Numismata Romanorum Pontificum* Rome 1744

Vidal Quadras y Ramon, M. *Catalogo de la Coleccion de Monedas y Medallas* Barcelona 1892

Vienna. *Katalog der Münzen- und Medaillen-Stem-pelsammlung* Vienna 1901-02

Vossberg, F. A. *Münzgeschichte der Stadt Danzig* Berlin 1852

Weber, F. P. *Aspects of Death* London 1922

Will, G. A. *Nürnbergische Münzbelustigungen* Altdorf 1764-66

Zeitschrift für Bildende Kunst Berlin 1889-

SALES CATALOGUES
TO WHICH
REFERENCE IS MADE

Ampach, Chr. L. Leipzig and Naumburg 1833-35

Belli, Ludwig Rosenberg and Shott-Wallerstein Frankfurt 1904-05

British Museum Duplicates Sotheby London 1922

Crona, Sune Eberhard Schlessinger Amsterdam 1937

Delbecke, August Hess Frankfurt 1891

Desmoni, Martin J. Sotheby London 1960

Donebauer, Max Hess Frankfurt 1889

Elkan, Münzhandlung Basel 1934

Engelhardt, Erbstein Dresden 1888-1909

Erbstein, J. and A. Hess Frankfurt 1908

Faure, Maurice L. Hamburger Frankfurt 1913

Felix, Eugen Hess Frankfurt 1895

Frankiewicz, M. Schlessinger Berlin 1930

Gallet, Georges Florange-Ciani Paris 1924

Gutekunst, Commerzienrat H. G. Dr. Jacob Hirsch Munich 1910

Hamburger, L. & L. Frankfurt 1891

———— L. Frankfurt 1922

Henckel, P. Berlin 1876

Lanna, Freiherr Adalbert von Lepke Berlin 1911. Parts II and III

Le Maistre Pax in Nummis Schulman Amsterdam 1912

Loebbecke, Arthur Dr. Jacob Hirsch Munich 1908

———— Riechmann Halle 1925

———— Schulman Amsterdam 1929

Merzbacher, Eugen Munich 1900 and 1914

Molthein, Alfred Walcher Ritter von Helbing Mu-nich 1926

Montenuovo, Prince Hess Frankfurt 1895

Mueller-Lebanon, Hans Cahn Frankfurt 1925

Neuburg, Schulman Amsterdam 1938

Oppenheimer, Henry Christie London 1936

Reimmann, Justizrat Hess Frankfurt 1891-92

Rosenheim, Max and Maurice Sotheby London 1923

Sambon, Dr. Arthur Dr. Jacob Hirsch Munich 1914

Schulthess-Rechberg, K. G. Ritter von Erbstein Dresden 1868-69

Spitzer, Frederic Paris and London 1893

Trau, Franz Egger Vienna 1904

Vogel, Geheimrat Hermann Hamburger Frankfurt 1924

Whitcombe-Greene, T. Sotheby London 1932

INDEX OF ARTISTS

Abondio, Alessandro, note preceding 112

Abondio, Antonio, 75, 112, 113

Alari Bonacolsi, Pier Jacopo di Antonio, see Antico

Altdorfer, Albrecht, 185

Antico, 14, 157

Antonio da Brescia, Fra, 9

Beham, Hans Sebald, note preceding 138, 140

Belli, Valerio, 52

Bernardi, Giovanni, 164

Bertinet, 85

Bertoldo di Giovanni, 24, 28

Blum, Johann, 124

Boldù, Giovanni di Pasqualino, 18

Bonzagna, Gian Federigo, see Parmense

Botticelli, Sandro, 28, note preceding 30

Braun, Johann Bartholomaeus, 125

Brescia, Fra Antonio de, see Antonio

Briosco, Andrea, see Riccio

Buchheim, Johann, 126

Camelio, see Gambello

Candida, Giovanni di Salvatore Filangieri, 27

Caradosso, Cristoforo, 23

Castelbolognese, Giovanni Bernardi da, see Bernardi

Cavino, Giovanni dal, 53-62

Cellini, Benvenuto, 36, 75, 79, note preceding 114

Cesati, Alessandro, see Grechetto

Cormano, Giovanni Jacopo, see Kornmann

Cranach, Lucas, note preceding 94, 94

Dadler, Sebastian, 117-119

De Laune, Etienne, 79

Deschler, Joachim, 90-92, 138

Donatello, note preceding 28

Drentwett, Balduin, 110, 111

Duccio, Agostino di, 156

Dürer, Albrecht, 86, 184

Duerr, Ernst Caspar, note preceding 132

Dupré Guillaume, note preceding 43, 81-83, note preceding 84

Elertz, Cornelius, note preceding 114

Enderlein, Caspar, 112

Enzola, Gianfrancesco, 16

Filangieri, Giovanni di Salvatore, see Candida

Fiorentino, Niccolo, see Spinelli

Foppa, Cristoforo Caradosso, see Caradosso

Franceschi, Piero dei, 10

Francia, Francesco, 22

Galeotto, see Romano, Pietro Paolo

Gambello, Vettor di Antonio, 19, 159-161

Gennaro, Maria Antonio di, 133

Geremia, Cristoforo di, note preceding 25

Ghibellini, Orazio, note preceding 49

Goedecke, Paul Heinrich, 135

Grechetto, 46

Guacialoti, Andrea, 24, note preceding 28

Hagenauer, Friedrich, 88, 89, 101

Hamerani, Alberto, note preceding 51

Hamerani, Giovanni, 51

Herclas, J., 154

Hirschvogel, Augustin, note preceding 138

Hoehn, Johann, 128-130

Hohenauer, Michel, 93

Holbein the Younger, Hans, note preceding 87, note preceding 138

Holdermann, Georg, 98, 99

Hollande, Etienne de, 75

IO.F.F., see Master IO.F.F.

Jamnitzer, Wenzel, note preceding 97

Januario, see Gennaro

Jonghelinck, Jacob, 142

Kitzkatz, Ruprecht Niclas, 116

Kornmann, Johann Jacob, 120

Leclerc, Nicolas, 78

Leoni, Leone, 65-67, note preceding 68, note preceding 142

Le Pere, Jean and Colin, 78

Lippi, Filippino, 15

Lutma, Jan Filius, 147

Lysippus the Younger, 25, 26

Maler, Valentin, 97, 110

Mantegna, Andrea, 158

Marescotti, Antonio, 5, 6

Master IO.F.F., 162

Memling, Hans, note preceding 27

Michelangelo, note preceding 28, note preceding 112

Michelino, Domenico di, 35

Milicz, Nickel, 138-140

Mocetto, Girolamo, 158

Moderno, 137, 159-161

Mola, Gaspare, 43, 44, note preceding 49

Moro, Jacobo Antonio, note preceding 43

Morone-Mola, Gasparo, 49

Mueller, Philipp Heinrich, 131

Muller, O. Wouter, 145, 146

Nuernberger, Paul Gottlieb, 134

Omeis, Martin Heinrich, 132

Padovano, see Cavino

Parise, Erich, 153

Parmense, Federigo, 47, 48, 165, 166

Pasti, Matteo di Maestro Andrea de', 10-13

Pastorino di Giovanni Michele de' Pastorini, 37, 38

Pfruendt, Anna Maria, note preceding 125

Pietro da Fano, 18

Pilon, Germain, 80

Pisanello, 1-4, 6

Pisano, Antonio, see Pisanello
Poggini, Domenico, 40
Poggini, Gianpaolo, 39, 40
Pool, Jurriaan, 144
Raibolini, Francesco, see Francia
Rantwic, Bernard, 151
Reinhart the Elder, Hans, 94-96, 137
Riccio, 158
Robbia, Andrea della, 34
Romano, Giancristoforo, 15
Romano, Pietro Paolo, 41, 42, 73
Rull, K., 155
Saint-Priest, Jean de, 78
Sansovino, Jacopo, note preceding 64, 163
Schega, Franz Andreas, 136
Selvi, Antonio, 45
Soldani-Benzi, Massimiliano, note preceding 45
Sperandio, 17
Spinelli, Andrea, 63
Spinelli, Niccolo di Forzore, note preceding 27, 30-34
Titian, note preceding 65, 67
Travani, Gioacchino Francesco, 50
Trezzo, Jacopo Nizzola da, 68
Vianen, Paul van, 114
Vicentino, see Belli
Vittoria, Alessandro, 64
Volpe, Vittoria della, see Vittoria
Warin, Jean, 84
Weiditz, Christoph, 87
Welcz, Concz, 137
Werner, Peter Paul, 134

INDEX OF PERSONS

REPRESENTED OR MENTIONED

Adrian VI, Pope, 150
Aelius, Roman emperor, 52
Agrippina Sr., Roman empress, 54
Alidosi, Francesco degli, 22
Alighieri, Dante, 35
Allgaeuer, Hieronymus, 109
Anne of Brittany, 78
Antonini, Floriano, 53
Ariosto, Lodovico, 37
Astallia, Giulia, 14
Augustus, Roman emperor, 167
Bandello, Matteo, 14
Barberini, Maffeo, 82
Behaim von Schwarzbach, Frederick, 105
Bellini, Giovanni, 19

Bembo, Pietro, 15
Bentivoglio, Giovanni II, 21
Bernhard of Saxe-Weimar, 124
Borgia, Lucrezia, 15
Caesarius, Johann, 107
Caligula, Roman emperor, 177
Caracalla, Roman emperor, 18
Caraffa, Antonio, 66, 68
Chamemilon, Euphrosina de, 104
Charles I, Count Palatine, 111
Charles V, Emperor, 42, note preceding 65, 67, 138
Charles VIII, King of France, 78
Charles X Gustav, King of Sweden, 154
Charles Ferdinand, Bishop of Breslau, note preceding 126
Christian I of Saxony, 116
Christian William of Brandenburg, 120
Christina, Queen of Sweden, 50
Contughi, Fra Cesario, 17
Cornaro, Fra Giovanni, 20
Cortez, Hernan, 87
Dante, see Alighieri
Delen, Nicholas van, 143
Dido, Queen of Carthage, 46
Dondi, Giovanni, 67
Donellus (Doneau), Hugo, 99
Doria, Andrea, note preceding 65
Dürer, Agnes, 86
Ehrenberg, Philipp Adolf von, 98
Elizabeth I, Queen of England, 152
Este, Alfonso II d', 38
Este, Lionello d', 3, 4
Evertsen, Cornelis, 146
Farnese, Pierluigi, 47
Faustina Jr., Roman empress, 61, 157
Ferdinand I, Emperor, 93, 138
Ferdinand III, Emperor, 123
Fetzer, Matthaeus, 97
Floriano, see Antonini
Francis I, King of France, 180
Frederick III, King of Denmark and Norway, 118, 153
Frederick V, King of Denmark and Norway, 135
Frederick Christian of Poland, 136
Frederick William I of Brandenburg, 134
Frundsberg, Anna von, 101
Gabrielli, Trifone, 70
Gamberia, Bernardino, 31
Gazzuolo, Giulia de, see Astallia
George III of Silesia, Liegnitz and Brieg, 126
Geraldini, Antonio, 30
Giovio, Paolo, 16

Gonzaga, Ippolita, 66, 68
Gonzaga, Vincenzo II, 49
Grimani, Marino, 74
Gritti, Andrea, 63, 169
Gustav II Adolf, King of Sweden, 121, 122, 155
Hanna, Daniel de, 65
Henry II, King of France, 79, note preceding 80
Henry III, King of France and Poland, 80
Henry IV, King of France, 81, 181
Hevelius, John, 130
Holzschuher, Sigmund Gabriel, 125
Innocent VIII, Pope, 30
Innocent XII, Pope, 51
John Casimir, King of Poland, 128, 129
John Frederick of Saxony, 94
John George I of Saxony, note preceding 117, note
    preceding 126
John George III of Saxony, 132
Julius II, Pope, 22
Khevenhueller, Johann, 112
Leo X, Pope, note preceding 159
Leopold I, Emperor, 127
Le Tellier, Michel, 85
Louis II, King of Hungary, 93
Louis VI, Count Palatine, 115
Louis XII, King of France, 78
Louis XIV, King of France, note preceding 84, 85
Lucius Verus, Roman emperor, 62
Lucretia, 86
Luther, Martin, 88, 110
Malatesta, Sigismondo Pandolfo, 10-13
Marciana, sister of Trajan, Roman emperor, 59
Marcus Aurelius, Roman emperor, 60
Maria of Aragon, 4
Maria of Burgundy, 27
Maria of Hungary, 93
Maximilian I, Emperor, 21, 27, 78
Maximilian II, Emperor, 112, 113, 139
Mazarin, Jean, 85
Medici, Catherine de', note preceding 80
Medici, Cosimo de' (Il Vecchio), note preceding 30
Medici, Cosimo I de', 36, 40, 45
Medici, Cosimo II de', 44
Medici, Lorenzo and Giuliano de', 28
Medici, Lucrezia de', 38
Medici, Marie de, Queen of France, 81, 83
Melanchthon, Philipp, 89
Memmo, Marcantonio, 82
Mendoza, Ambassador of Ferdinand and Isabella, 30
Menno van Friesland, 88
Musso, Cornelio, 73
Mylius (Miler), Georg, 110

Nale, Giovanni di, 69
Nero, Roman emperor, note preceding 30
Nerva, Roman emperor, 58
Neudoerfer, Johann, 91
Opdam van Wassenaer, Baron, 154
Otho, Roman emperor, 55
Panigarola, Francesco, 76
Paumgartner, Hieronymus, 90
Perrenot, Antoine, 142
Philip II, King of Spain, 39
Piantanida, Pietro, 75
Piccolomini, Alessandro, 36
Pisano, Antonio, 6
Pius V, Pope, 48
Primislav, King of Bohemia, 133
Priuli, Girolamo, 72
Rangoni, Tommaso, 64
Remo, Opizo, 9
Richelieu, Armand Jean de, 84
Rinuccini, Alamanno, 32
Rovere, Francesco Maria della, 22
Rudolf II, Emperor, 114
Savonarola, Girolamo, 34
Savoy, Charles Emanuel I, 43
Schwarzbach, Frederick Behaim von, see Behaim
Sforza, Faustina, 41
Sforza, Francesco, 2, 16
Sforza, Ludovico Maria, 23
Shelley, Sir Richard, 151
Sixtus IV, Pope, 24, 25, 168
Sophia of Brandenburg, 116
Sophia Amalia of Brunswick, 153
Spinola de Serravalis, Battista, 77
Strozzi, Tito Vespasiano, 29
Suleiman I, Ottoman sultan, 93
Sybille of Saxony, 103
Tannhausen, Emerentiana von, 102
Tavelli, see Tossignano
Tiberius, Roman emperor, 176
Titus, Roman emperor, 57
Toledo, Eleonora de, 36
Torre, Gianello della, 67
Toscani, Giovanni Alvise, 26
Tossignano, Giovanni Tavelli da, 5
Trajan, Roman emperor, 179
Trevisan, Marcantonio, 71
Trivulzio, Gianfrancesco, 42
Trivulzio, Giangiacomo, 22, 23, 42
Tromp, Martin Harpertszoon, 144, 145
Unknown persons:
    Boy, 8
    Humanist, 88, 107

Man, 7
Mohammedan, 108
Patrician, 100, 106
Urban VIII, Pope, 82
Vecchietti, Alessandro di Gino, 33
Vespasian, Roman emperor, 178
Virgil, 24
Visconti, Filippo Maria, 1
Vitellius, Roman emperor, 56
Vitil, Wolfgang, 106
Vondel, Joost van den, 147
Waldstein, John Frederick, 141
Waldstein, John Henry, 133
Waldstein, John Joseph, 133
William III and Mary, King and Queen of England, 131
Wladislas II, King of Hungary, 93

INDEX OF INSCRIPTIONS

A D (monogram), 86
Ad civitat ditionisq tvtel mvnim extrvctvm, 47
A deo et pro deo, 51
A d ianvario f, 133
Aet 39, 42
Aetatis svae 65 franciae orientalis dvx, 92
Aeternitati sacrvm, 53
Agrippina m f mat c caesaris avgvsti, 54
A iove et sorore genita, 64
A L (monogram), 112
Alamannvs rinvccinvs philippi f, 32
Alessandro di gino vechietti anni Z6, 33
All mein hofnvng zv got, 97
An Ab, 112
And griti m venet dvx, 169
Andreas griti dvx venetiar mdxxxiiii, 63
Anna georgi in frvntsperg vxor, 101
Anno do mi mdxci, 111
An sp f, 63
Antonii perrenot epi atrebat, 142
Antoninvs pivs avgvstvs, 18
Antonivs geraldinvs pontificivs logotheta fastorvm vates, 30
Archi dvx avstri dvx bvrg marc mor 1566, 139
Armandvs ioannes cardinalis de richeliev, 84
Aurea florigeris succrescunt poma rosettis, 131
A vitellivs german imp avg p m tr, 56
Bap spinola d serravallis, 77
Ber gamb innocentii viii c s an xxx 1485, 31
Bern rantwic f, 151
Blum, 124
B nicolavs van delen, 143

Bo fphff en, 15
Brisach fortis sed fortior deus fvit et weimarius 1638, 124
Cap pet plantanida aet an xxxvi, 75
Car d g co pa rhe ba dv c v e s, 111
Carolvs eman d g dvx sab p p, 43
Castellvm sismondvm ariminense mccccxlvi, 10
Castellvm sismvndvm ariminense mccccxlvi, 13
C caes t d, 177
Christum hat gott furgestelt zu einem gnadenstuel, 117
Chrvs moritvr pro nobis et resvrgit vt nos ivstos faciat 46, 137
Coelitus data, 132
Comes de waldstein, 141
Congiar p r, 58
Consecratio s p q r, 59
Consilio et indvstria, 127
Cornelivs mvssvs ep bitvnt, 73
Cosmvs med floren et senar dvx ii, 40
Daniel de hanna, 65
Danthes florentinvs, 35
Das hoeheste gut, 118
D'eta di xxxiii anni mdxliiii, 69
Devm cole avrvm contemne virtvtem sectare argentvm sperne patriam defende 16Z9, 121
Devotissimvs pavper pr d iohanes eps ferrarienm, 5
Dextera tva dom percvssit inimicvm 1571, 48
D georgivs mylivs avg aet 31, 110
D g georg dux sil l & b supremae pers il praef administr, 126
D g sophia nat mar bran dvc sax ele, 116
Dido basilissa, 46
Diva avgvsta marciana, 59
Diva favstina, 157
Diva ivlia astallia, 14
Divi francisci mdxxxiiii, 63
Divinvm concinit orbi, 73
D martinus lutherus, 88
D martinvs lvtervs, 110
Dominvs providebit, 153
Dominvs 1570 providebit, 113
Don ferdinando cortes mdxxix anno etatis xxxxii, 87
Dvm spiritvs hos reget artvs, 75
Dvrate, 142
Ego sicvt oliva frvctificavi sva vitae odo i do di, 5
E P, 153
Etatis sve 30, 93
Et sicvt in adam omnes morivntvr ita et in christvm omnes vivificabvntvr vnvs qvisqve in ordine svo, 95
Et victricibvs armis, 122

Evphrosina de chamemilon, 104
Exemplvm vnicvm for et pvd, 14
Expvgnata alexandria deleto exercitv lvdovicvm sf
    mli dvc expellit reversvm apvd nova riam sternit
    capit, 23
Externo male pressa iugo britannia pridem in priscas
    iterum respirat libera leges, 131
F a schega f, 136
Favstina avg antonini avg pii fil, 61
Favstina sfortia march caravagii, 41
Felice lvdovico regnante dvodecimo cesare altero
    gavdet omnis nacio, 78
Ferdinandvs d g romanor hvngari boemini infans
    hispa arc avs rex 1550, 138
Ferd iii d g rom hvng bohem r "etc.," 123
Feris tantvm infensvs, 49
Fert, 43
Firmavit omen, 114
Florianvs antoninvs andreae f, 53
F p, 48
F parm, 47
Fr alidoxivs car papien bon romandiolae q c legat, 22
Francesco panigarola aeta anni xxviii, 76
Fr cesarivs fer ordins ser b m v divin l t exellen doc
    ac divi ver famosis predicator, 17
Frideric christ d g pr reg pol & lith dux sax & el, 136
Fridericus iii d g dan norw got vand rex dux sl holst
    dit com in old & delm, 118
Fridericvs d g eps wircebvrg, 92
Frid wilh d g rex borvss el brand, 134
Fried v dg rex dan norv van go, 135
Fr sfortia vicecomes mli dvx iiii belli pater et pacis
    avtor mcccclvi, 16
F s k i p f t, 6
Fvi svm et ero, 42
Gasp m, 43
G dupre 1615, 83
G dupre f 1612, 82
Giovanni di nale, 69
Gladivs domini svp teram citoet velociter, 34
G moron f, 49
Gott lies adam hart entschla nam ein ripp a s s m d d
    eva g z, 140
Greek inscriptions:
    Karchedon, 46
    Leon aretinos, 66
    Makelos, 50
Gust adol d g svec got vand rex m prin fin dv eth et
    car ig d, 155
Gvilielmvs et maria rex et regina britaniae, 131
Gvstavvs adolp d g svec goth wand q rex, 121, 122
Hac secvla ivbilant vmbra, 135

Hafnia daniae, 154
Hamera, 51
Hebrew inscriptions:
    Name of God, 121, 122
    Oh Lord, help us, 77
Hec damvs in terris aeterna dabvntvr olimpo, 25
Heer everts met triomf "etc.," 146
Henricvs ii francor rex invictiss p p, 79
Henricvs 3 d g fran et pol rex 1575, 80
Henricvs iiii d g franc et navar rex, 81
Heroica foecunditas, 133
Herois huius nomina in cuncta clarent secula, 124
Hier stryckt het britsch gewelt "etc.," 146
Hieronimvs priol ve dvx, 72
Hieronx[!]mvs savo fer vir doctisss ordinis predicha-
    torvm, 34
Hieronymvs allgoewer xviil iar alt a mdlvi, 109
Hieronymvs pavmgartner anno aetatis 56, 90
Hippolyta gonzaga ferdinandi fil an xvi, 66
Hippolyta gonzaga ferdinandi fil an xvii, 68
His avibvs cvrrvq citodvce ris ad astra, 22
H R 1536, 95
Hvgo donellvs ic cl prof aldorp aet svae 64 an 90, 99
Iac trez, 68
Ianas qvi post tres dies de piste exivit designat cristi
    ressvrexionem capitvlo Z, 137
Ianellvs tvrrian cremon horolog architect, 67
I B, 126
I H, 128-130, 154
Imp caes maximil ii avg, 112
Imp nerva caes avg p m tr p cos ii p p, 58
Imp otho caesar avg tri pot, 55
Imp t caes vesp avg p m tr p p p cos viii, 57
Imp vii cos iii, 60
Indvstriam adivvat devs, 91
Innocen xii pont m a i, 51
Innocens manib et mvndo corde, 70
Inspice mortale genvs mors omnia delet, 17
In vmbra alarvm tvarvm sperabo donec transeat
    iniqvitas, 90
Ioan casim d g rex pol & suec m d l r prus, 129
Ioannes aloisivs tvsca avditor cam, 26
Ioannes bellinvs venet pictor op, 19
Ioannes bentivolvs ii bononiensis, 21
Ioannes casimirus d g poloniae & sueciae rex "etc.,"
    128
Ioannes frideric archie prag, 141
Ioanns fridericvs elector dvx saxonie fieri fecit, 95
Ioanns fridericvs elector dvx saxonie fieri fecit etatis
    svae 32, 94
Io cornelivs mona cor casin colvmen, 20
Io fran tri mar vig co mvso ac val ren et stosa d, 42

Io fr enzolae parmensis opvs, 16
Iohannes hevelius dantiscan "etc.," 130
Iohann nevdorffer arithm aet sve lvii, 91
Ioh georg iii d sax i c m a & w el, 132
Io iacobvs trivvls mar vig fra marescalvs, 23
Io son fine, 18
I pavl pog f, 39
I pv an viii me ii di iiii obi a mdlxvii m n de iiii, 72
Ivdaea capta s c, 57
Ivdicivm dni apprehendit eos et fortitvdo eivs corro-
    boravit brachivm mevm, 87
Ivlianvs medices, 28
I warin 1630, 84
Jesus hat sich zum losegelt beim himlischen vatter
    dargestelt fur alle sund der gantzen welt, 117
Joost van den vondel gest 5 feb 1679, 147
J pool, 144
L aelivs caesar, 52
Lavrentivs medices, 28
Leonellvs marchio estensis, 3
Leonellvs marchio estensis ge r ar d ferrarie regii et
    mvtine, 4
Leopoldvs d g rom imperator, 127
Lievtenant admiraal van holland "etc.," 144
Lvcretia borgia esten ferrariae mvt ac regii d, 15
Lvcretia med ferr princ a a xiii, 38
Lvctvs pvblicvs, 28
Lvd d g co pa ele a d z, 115
Lvdovic vnga ec rex contra tvrca pvgnando occvbvit
    1526 etatis sve 30, 93
Lvdovicvs ariost poet, 37
L vervs avg arm parth max tr p viiii, 62
Lvgdvn repvblica gavde te bis anna regnante benigne
    sic fvi conflata 1499, 78
Magni ducis bernhardi saxon weim effigies, 124
Magnvs cosmvs medices p p p, 45
Maiestas maior ab igne, 81
M antoninvs avg tr p xxix, 60
Maph s r e p car barberin sig ivst prae bono leg, 82
Marcvs antonivs memmo dvx venetiarvm, 82
Marcvs antonivs trevixano dei gratia dvx venetiarvm
    etc vixitano i in principatv obit mdliiii, 71
Marcvs ant trevisano dvx v, 71
Marescotvs f, 5
Maria avg galliae et navarae regina, 83
Maria karoli f dvx bvrgvndiae avstriae barb c flan, 27
Maria regina ec qvos devs conivnxit homo non
    seperet, 93
Marin grimanvs dvx venetiar, 74
Marten harpertsen tromp ridder, 144
Mathevs fetzer aet li 1576, 97
Maximiliani imperatoris mvnvs mcccclxxxxiiii, 21

Maximilianvs fr caes f dvx avstr bvrgvnd, 27
Maximilianvs ii d g roma imperi sem avg ger hv bo
    etc rex, 139
Maximili ii rom i s av, 113
Mccccxliiii, 4
Mccccxlvi, 5, 10, 11, 13
Mccccxlvii, 12
Mcccclvi, 16
Mcccclxvi, 18
Mcccclxxxi, 24
Mcccclxxxxiiii, 21
Mdxxxiiii, 63
Mdxxxv, 94
Mdxxxxiii, 89
Mdxliiii, 69
Mdliiii, 71
Mdlvi, 109
Mdlix, 39
Mdlxvii, 72
Mdxci, 111
Mdcvi, 43
Mdclviii, 128
Mdccxxxiii, 134
Mdcclxiii, 136
Memoriae agrippinae, 54
Micha letellier fr cancellarivs 1678, 85
Mijn hert en hant was voor het lant, 145
Miserere nobis domine, 96
M M (monogram), 27
Monograms:
    A D, 86
    A L, 112
    M M, 27
Mvlier dedit mihi et comedi ge z, 96
N, 134
Nat dresdae d 20 iun ao 1647 denat tubingae ao 1691
    d 12 sept, 132
Nat 6 jun 1568 mor 7 dec 1622 pietas, 116
Nat 9 dec 1594 denat 6 nov 1632, 155
Nostra medela, 119
Numinis auspicys et regis fortibus armis "etc.," 128
Nvnq deficit, 67
Obiit v octobris mdcclxiii, 136
O f, 132
Oldenb dan tertia vice ivbilans d 28 oct 1749, 135
Omne vanvm, 65
Op ni fo sp fl, 30
Oportvne, 43
Opvs pisani pictoris, 1, 3
Opvs pisani pictoris mccccxliiii, 4
Opvs sperandei, 17

P, 38
Pace terra mariq composita, 39
Parcere svbiectis et debellare svperbos, 24
Parm invent, 165
Par vbiq potestas, 66
Patriarvm exvbitor opvm, 151
Pax aeterna ad gedan a cıɔɔcıx iii maii condita, 129
P H G, 135
Philipp adolph d g eps wirceb fr or dvx, 98
Philippvs hispaniar et novi orbis occidvi rex, 39
Philippvsmaria anglvs dvx mediolani etcetera papie anglerie qve comes ac genve dominvs, 1
Philippvs melanthon anno aetatis svae xlvii, 89
P H M, 131
Pietas evangelica, 20
Piis manibus aug iii magnanimi, 136
Pisanvs pictor, 6
Pivs v pont opt max anno vi, 48
P loysivs f parm et plac dvx i, 47
P m adriaen van god ghekoren pavs van romen t'utrecht gheboren, 150
Pontificii exercitvs imp mccccxlvii, 12
P p a e, 168
P p werner fec, 134
Privs mori qvam tvrpari, 33
Pro bono malvm, 37
Pro deo et milite, 134
Progenies divvm qvintvs sic carolvs ille imperii caesar lvmina aet svae l, 138
Psal 36 svbditvs esto deo et ora evm anno mdxxxxiii, 89
Quorum memoriam ioan ios com a waldstein "etc.," 133
Qvamvis occvmbas felix occvmbis in ipso stare tvam effigiem sol oriente vides, 123
Qvo melior optabilior, 40
Regina christina, 50
Religio sancta, 30
Ren als in eren, 94
Ricardvs scelleivs prior angliae, 151
Rvdolphvs ii rom imp avg rex hvng boe, 114
Sacrae romanae ecclesiae capitanvs generalis, 10, 11
Salvs pvblica, 28
Satiabor cvm apparverit, 31
S C, 52, 56-58, 61
S D, 117, 118
Securitas britaniae restituta 1689, 131
Secvritas p r, 55
Seht wie der fried iez ziert die welt "etc.," 118
Semper, 45
Senats popls, 157

Seren d d ioh georg elect sax in matr chariss, 116
Serenitatis nvncia, 123
Servando dea facta deos, 83
Sibila iohanni friderichi dvcis vxor saxoniae, 103
Sigismondvs pandvlfvs de malatestis s ro eclesie c generalis, 10, 11
Sigismvndvs pandvlfvs malatesta, 12
Sigismvndvs pandvlfvs malatesta pan f, 13
Sigm gabriel holzschvher ae 67, 125
Sixte potes, 24
Sixtvs papa iiii, 168
Sixtvs iiii pon max sacri cvlt, 24
Sixtvs iiii pont max sacri cvlt, 25
S'lants outste en grootste poeet geb 17 nov 1587, 147
Sors mea a domino, 126
Spe gloriae hvmilis, 125
Spes mea in deo, 153
Spes mea in deo est, 95
Spes mea in deo est anno nostri salvatoris mdxxxv, 94
S p q r, 54, 59
Stans acie pvgnans vincens moriensq trivmphat, 155
Svbditvs esto deo et ora evm anno mdxxxxiii, 89
Sydera cordis, 74
Tandem victa seqvor, 84
Te copia lavro et fama bearvnt nvia, 79
Thom philol raven phys eq gvard d mar mag, 64
Thve recht fvrchte gott vnd niemants mehr, 120
Tiber caesar, 176
Titvs strocivs, 29
Tr p vii imp iiii cos iii p p, 62
Tryphon gabriel, 70
Vespasian avg c, 178
Vff der hochzeit zv cana verwandelt christvs wasse z w io z, 140
V g g c w p a b e v s m v h p g m z b i p h, 120
Vic avg, 60
Victa iam nvrsia fatis agitvr, 26
Victor camelivs faciebat, 19
Vincen ii d g dvx mant vii et m f v, 49
Vinces virtvte viventis 1580, 115
Virtvs, 67
Virtvti ac formae pvdicitia praeciosissimvm, 15
Virtvtis et ingenii, 19
Virtvtis formaeq praevia, 68
Vt moses erexit serpente ita chrs in crvce exaltatvs et resvscitatvs capvt serpentis contrivit salvaret credentes, 95
Vulner christi, 119
Waarom doet muller tromp door kunst "etc.," 145
XXIV filii a patre ioan henrico barone "etc.," 133

GENERAL INDEX

Adam and Eve, 35, 95, 96
Adoration of the Magi, see Christ
Adoration of the shepherds, see Christ
Aeneas, sinking of his ship, 142
Alexandria, capture of, 23
Amor, 4, 15
Antwerp, Memling, Portrait of man holding coin, note preceding 27
Archer, see Astronomy, Sagittarius
Architecture and buildings, 10, 13, 40, 46, 47, 53, 61, 63, 165, 166
Arm holding birch rod, 12
Arms, coat of:
  Este, 3
  Fetzer, 97
  Florence, 36
  Gonzaga, 49
  Holzschuher, 125
  Liegnitz-Brieg, 126
  Lyon, 78
  Neudoerfer, 91
  Paumgartner, 90
  Pope Adrian VI, 150
  Richelieu, 84
  Savoy, 43
  Saxony, 94-96
  Sforza, Francesco, 16
  Trivulzio, 23
  Van Delen, 143
  Vecchietti, 33
  Visconti, 1, 23
  Wuerzburg, 92, 98
Asti, medal referring to, 76
Astronomy:
  Capricorn, 114
  Comets, 130
  Lunar maps, 130
  Pisces, 22
  Sagittarius, 22, 43
Augsburg, medals made in, or referring to, 87-89, 106, 110, 111, 131
Aurora riding chariot drawn by Pegasus, 68
Battle scenes, 48, 144, 145, 146, 154, 164
Bees surrounding a column, 37
Biscione, 1
Bolla, 168, 169
Bologna, medals made in, or referring to, 15, 21, 22, 23, 34, 82
Breisach, capture of, 124
Burgundy, medal made for the Court of, 27
Cachet, 143
Cana, marriage at, 140

Cannae, battle of, 164
Capitanus Generalis, title of Malatesta, 10, 11
Caritas, standing, 51
Carthage, view of, 46
Chariot:
  drawn by eagles, 22
  drawn by Pegasus, 68
  Fame, riding in, 79, 84
  funerary, 54, 59
  Poseidon in, 142
  Wisdom, riding in, 182
Chateau Cambresis, Peace treaty of, 39
Checkers, 101-108
Chiron, the centaur, 43
Christ:
  Nativity, 148
  Adoration of the shepherds, 165
  Adoration of the Magi, 148
  Flight into Egypt, 185
  carrying the cross, 117, 119, 170, 183
  Crucifixion, 95, 96, 159, 160
  wearing the crown of thorns, 119
  Pietà, 156
  Entombment, 166, 171, 173, 184
  Resurrection, 115, 137
  head of, 174, 175
Combat, Roman, 161, 164
Constantia, standing, 24
Constellations, see Astronomy
Copenhagen, siege and relief of, 154
Cremona, 67
Crucifixion, see Christ
Cupid, see Amor
Death, 17, 18
Denmark and Norway, medals made in, or referring to, 118, 135, 153, 154
Diana, accompanied by three hunting dogs, 66
Dog, see Greyhound, Hound
Downs, battle of the, 145
Eagle:
  Biga of eagles, 22
  facing, holding globe, 113
  flying towards Sun, 114
  perched on leafless tree, 4
Elephant:
  Order of the, 118
  Seat formed by two, 11
England, medals made in, or referring to, 131, 141, 145, 146, 151, 152
Entombment, see Christ
Equestrian figures, 1, 112
Ermine, 78

Eve, creation of, 140, see also Adam and Eve
Faith, standing, 75
Fall of Man, 95, 96
Fame, riding in quadriga, 79, 84
Ferrara, medals made in, or referring to, 3-9, 15, 17, 34, 38
Fleur-de-lis, 36, 78, 180
Flight into Egypt, see Christ
Florence, Duomo of, 28, 35
Florence, medals and plaquettes made in, or referring to, 24, 28-45, 156, 167
Fortitude, seated, 11
Fortuna over waves, 33, 42; chained to quadriga, 84
Fountain, see Sciences, fountain of
France, medals and plaquettes made in, or referring to, 22, 23, 34, 78-85, 99, 180, 181
Frankfurt, coronation of Leopold I at, 127
Genoa, medals referring to, 1, 34, 77
God, the Father in clouds, 31, 159
Greyhound, seated, 16
Griffon, standing, 151
Hand with dagger, threatening from Heaven, 34
Hebe, the birth of, 64
Hound, Gonzaga device, 49; Hounds of Diana, 66
Horsemen, see Equestrian figures
Innocence, washing her hands at spring, 70
Italy:
    French invasion of, 22, 23, 34
    map of, 34
Janus, the closed temple of, 39
Jason and the dragon, 9
Jonas, the prophet, 137
Judaea, capture of, 57
Judith, 158
Jupiter:
    seated on the Seven Hills of Rome, 62
    wielding thunderbolt, in biga of eagles, 22
Lepanto, battle of, 48
Liberalitas, 58
Liberty, seated, 131
Lion:
    learning to sing, 4
    of St. Mark, 74
    rampant, 172
Low Countries, medals and plaquettes made in, or referring to, 114, 131, 142-150, 154, 182
Luetzen, battle of, 155
Lyon, entry of Louis XII and Anne of Brittany into, 78
Mantua, medals and plaquettes made in, or referring to, 14, 15, 17, 49, 66, 68, 157

Map:
    lunar, see Astronomy
    of Italy, 34
Marriage, 4, 27, 38, 78, 93, 140
Mars, striding, 56
Milan, medals made in, or referring to, 1, 2, 16, 23, 26, 34, 41, 65-68, 75-77
Minerva:
    Queen Christina as, 50
    standing, 111, 135
Modena, 15
Mohacs, battle of, 93
Music, 4, 15
Naples, medals referring to, 4, 34, 133
Nativity, see Christ
Neptune:
    in chariot, 26, 40
    sinking Aeneas' ship, 142
Netherlands, see Low Countries
Noerdlingen, battle of, 123
Nürnberg, medals and plaquettes made in, or referring to, 86, 90, 91, 97-100, 105, 125, 132, 134, 183-185
Oliva, Peace of, 129
Otranto, expulsion of the Turks from, 24
Owl, perched on branch, 19
Padua, medals and plaquettes made in, or referring to, 20, 52-62, 64, 158
Pallas Athena, see Minerva
Paris, Judgement of, 162
Parma, bird's-eye view of the citadel of, 47
Patientia, caressing lamb, 111
Pavia, battle of, 42
Pax:
    seated, 118
    setting fire to armaments, 39
Pazzi Conspiracy, note preceding 24, 28
Pelican, 20
Phoenix on pyre, 14, 50, 152
Pietà, see Christ
Pisa, medals referring to, 34
Pluto, seated, 66
Poland, medals referring to, 80, 128-130, 136
Poseidon, see Neptune
Prague, Kreuzherrenkirche at, 141
Purgatory, Dante before Mountain of, 35
Ravenna, 64
Reformation, 88, 89, 110
Religion, standing, 30, 122
Resurrection, see Christ
Rimini, castle of, 10, 13

Rocca Malatestiano, see Rimini
Roman emperors and empresses, 18, 52, 54-62, 157, 167, 176-179
Rome, medals and plaquettes made in, or referring to, 24, 25, 30, 31, 34, 46-51, 62, 82, 164-166, 168
Sagittarius, see Astronomy
Sail, impresa of, see Vela
St. Anthony, 25
St. Francis, 25, 186
St. George, spearing the dragon, 112
St. Mark, 169; lion of, 74
St. Paul, 168
St. Peter, 123, 168, 187
Saul, anointing of, 149
Savoy, medal of, 43
Sciences, Fountain of, 67
Seals, see Bolla and Cachet
Shepherd with sheep, 20
Ships:
    Aeneas', 142
    manned by four girls, 83
    on raging sea, 77, 142
    sea battles, 48, 144-146, 154
Siege of city, 23, 24, 124, 128
Sigillum, see Bolla
Spain, medals and plaquettes made in, or referring to, 39, 67, 87, 186, 187
Stone models, 36, 109

Sundial, 135
Swan with spread wings, 73
Sweden, medals referring to, 50, 121, 122, 124, 128, 154, 155
Tagus river, 67
Thirty Years' War, 118, 120-124, 155
Thorn, capture of, 128
Triumphal car, see Chariot
Triumphal procession, Roman, 157
Turkish Wars, 24, 48, 93, 108
Vanity, standing, 65
Vela, Este device, 3
Venice, medals and plaquettes made in, or referring to, 18-20, 34, 63, 64, 65, 70-74, 82, 159-161, 163, 169-172
Venice, view of the church of San Francesco della Vigna, 63
Vesta:
    seated, 59
    statue of, in temple, 61
Victory:
    crowning France, 84
    seated, 60
Virgin, coronation of the, 163
Wax, 100
Westphalia, Peace of, 118, 123
Wisdom, triumph of, 182
Würzburg, medals referring to, 92, 98

ONE THOUSAND FIVE HUNDRED COPIES OF
THIS CATALOGUE HAVE BEEN PRINTED AT
THE MERIDEN GRAVURE COMPANY, MERI-
DEN, CONNECTICUT. COMPOSITION BY THE
ANTHOENSEN PRESS, PORTLAND, MAINE.
PHOTOGRAPHY BY JOHN MCKEE. DESIGN
BY LEONARD BASKIN. OCTOBER MCMLXV.